Turning to Schrödinger's
writings, Dr. Scott considers
tempts of a brilliant scientist t
meaningful place for man in t
verse. Troubled by the failure of dualistic notions of mind and matter to
make sense in the face of experience,
Schrödinger adopted a monistic view,
making use of the Vedantic conception of the identity of the individual
self with a universal Self.

There were few limits to Erwin
Schrödinger's interests as a philosopher
and as a scientist. In this new study his
extensive works are shown to be significant contributions to the history of
ideas.

William T. Scott is professor of theoretical physics at the University of
Nevada. After receiving his degrees
from Swarthmore College and the
University of Michigan, he taught at
Amherst and Smith Colleges. His
writings include *The Physics of Electricity and Magnetism* (John Wiley,
1959, second edition, 1966) and numerous articles on the cosmic-ray
shower theory, the multiple scattering
of fast charged particles, and more recently, the physics of coalescing drop-
lets in clouds. Currently participating
in the atmospheric physics research
project of the Desert Research Institute of the University of Nevada, Dr.
Scott has conducted research at Yale
University, the National Bureau of
Standards, and the Brookhaven National Laboratory.

his theories. Students interested in the
philosophical foundations of quantum
theory, and in efforts to modify or
rationalize it, will find important insights in this account of Schrödinger's
thought.

ERWIN SCHRÖDINGER

An Introduction to
His Writings

ERWIN SCHRÖDINGER

An Introduction to His Writings

William T. Scott

UNIVERSITY OF
MASSACHUSETTS PRESS
1967

To Michael Polanyi

Preface

If Erwin Schrödinger's only contribution to physics were wave mechanics, a study of the development of his thought which culminated in this great discovery would still be of interest. But Schrödinger did far more than further our comprehension of nature at the atomic level. In a profound way he challenged physicists to think more deeply about quantum mechanics, that highly successful yet disturbing theory of atomic and nuclear systems of which his wave mechanics is an important expression. Although not many physicists agree with his insistence on the continuous aspects of the theory as against the discrete or "energy-level" aspects, we are all indebted to his profound questioning.

Even more, his lucid insights into almost every branch of physics, as well as into the epistemological questions of how we arrive at our understanding of the physical world, are a challenge to all serious students.

Erwin Schrödinger went beyond questions of the objective world of physics to ask himself the most profound and existential question of all— "Who am I?" He sought clues to the nature of the self, both in the content of scientific observations about the physical and biological worlds, e.g., in discussing freedom and determinism and in thinking of man as knower. Man is part of the world he studies; in Schrödinger's view, man's science is at bottom a kind of self-knowledge.

Such is the breadth and complexity of Schrödinger's scholarship that to present a complete account of his life and thought would be a major undertaking. As a modest introduction I have tried to present here a connected account of a considerable portion of his work. I have selected the several areas of atomic and statistical physics that led up to wave mechanics, the famous theory itself, and the later developmental and critical work that is related to it. I have also included a brief biography, an account of most of his nontechnical writing, and a bibliography of his work. An outline of the many areas in which Schrödinger wrote is to be found in the first chapter. My sources have been his published writings, and I have not attempted to incorporate the wealth of private papers and recorded interviews that are just now becoming available through the efforts of the joint project of the American Physical and Philosophical Societies, "Sources for History of Quantum Physics." I hope that the present work will assist in later efforts to combine both the published and unpublished sources into a definitive account.

The book is primarily written for physicists, physics students, and philosophers of science who have had some introduction to the theories of statistical physics and wave mechanics, but at least Chapters I and V may be of interest to the general reader who wishes to know more about Schrödinger's life and world view.

The writing of this book was prompted by a suggestion made by Professor Henry Margenau during my sabbatical year at Yale University, 1959–60. I was intrigued by the possibility of dealing with interpretive questions in quantum mechanics along the lines of Margenau's work. Hence came the proposal to investigate Schrödinger's interpretation of wave mechanics and to look into his philosophical and other nontechnical writings.

The work was completed with the assistance of a grant from the National Science Foundation which enabled me to spend two additional summers at Yale. There I had the continued assistance and encouragement of Henry Margenau, the use of the facilities of the Yale Library, and the hospitality of the department of physics. My heartfelt thanks are due Professor Margenau, Yale University, and the National Science Foundation for this privilege.

I also wish to express my gratitude to the National Science Foundation for the Science Faculty Fellowship which supported me for six months in 1960 and to my children Jennifer and Christopher for their assistance in correlating bibliographic references. I greatly appreciate the kind efforts of Professor Michael Polanyi of Oxford, who read my work critically, and the many helpful suggestions of Professor Erling Skorpen of the University of Nevada on the content of the last chapter. Any weaknesses or inaccuracies remaining in the book are, of course, my own responsibility. To Mrs. Steven Kaylor go my thanks for assistance with the typing. Lastly, I wish to acknowledge the most valuable and en-

Preface

couraging assistance of my wife, Ann, who is largely responsible for whatever clarity and facility are shown by the writing, especially in Chapters I and V. Without her help it is doubtful whether this book could have been brought to satisfactory completion.

WILLIAM T. SCOTT

Reno, Nevada
May, 1966

Acknowledgments

To Cambridge University Press for permission to quote from *What is Life?* (1952), *Science and Humanism: Physics in Our Time* (1951), *Nature and the Greeks* (1954), *Mind and Matter* (1958), and *My View of the World* (1964). To Dover Publications, Inc. for permission to quote from *Science Theory and Man* (1957).

Contents

Contents

Abbreviations

The following abbreviations for books by Erwin Schrödinger are used throughout. Full details are to be found in the Bibliography.

AW	*Abhandlung zur Wellenmechanik* (1927)
WM	*Collected Papers on Wave Mechanics* (1928)
SHT	*Science and the Human Temperament* (1935)
SH	*Science and Humanism: Physics in our Time* (1951)
NG	*Nature and the Greeks* (1954)
WIL	*What is Life? and Other Scientific Essays* (1956)
STM	*Science Theory and Man* (1957)
MM	*Mind and Matter* (1958)
WN	*Was ist ein Naturgesetz? Beiträge zum naturwissenschaftlichen Weltbild* (1962)
MVW	*My View of the World* (1964)

Chapter I

Erwin Schrödinger, Physicist
and Philosopher

Erwin Schrödinger was born in Vienna on August 12, 1887. By background and upbringing he was a true Viennese, and remained one throughout his life. The Schrödinger family was part of the joyous and vigorous intellectual life of this capital city of the Old Danube Monarchy where, at the turn of the century, the advancement of culture counted more than achievement in business or politics. Although Schrödinger's father, Rudolf, ran the family linoleum business with considerable success, his deepest interests lay elsewhere. He was trained in botany and was the author of a series of articles on plant genetics. For a time in his youth he enthusiastically pursued the subject of Italian painting, even making some etchings and landscape drawings of his own. He also studied chemistry under Alexander Bauer, a professor at the Technische Hochschule whose middle daughter he was later to marry. As friend, teacher, and tireless partner in conversation, Rudolf Schrödinger shared his lively intellectual life with his son and only child. Looking back on his childhood, Erwin Schrödinger remembered his father as the "Court of Appeal" for all subjects of interest.[1]

Until he reached the age of 11 and entered a Gymnasium, the young Schrödinger's formal education was carried on at home under the guidance of a private tutor. Along with their formality and rigidity, the best Gymnasiums of that period provided a sound classical education, as well as elementary training in mathematics and physics. As we would expect, Schrödinger was fond of the latter subjects, but he also loved poetry and drama and "the strict logic of ancient philology" (*die strenge Logik der*

---

[1] "Erwin Schrödinger," autobiographical sketch in *Les Prix Nobel en 1933*, M. C. G. Santesson, ed. (Stockholm: Imprimerie Royale, P. A. Norstedt en Söner), p. 86.

alten Grammatiken).[2] Routine memorization he hated, as he was later to dislike the uncreative development of detail, but nevertheless he was regularly first in his class.

Schrödinger's maternal grandmother was English, and his fluency in that language developed in his childhood. In later years he not only spoke and wrote frequently in English (including six-sevenths of his papers after 1934), but, what is more impressive, he was a master of English style and wit. He was also at home in other languages and delivered his lectures, depending on his audience, in English, German, French, or Spanish. Schrödinger's early interest in the classics remained with him thoughout his life. His friend Hans Thirring mentions his translation of Homer from the original into English and of old Provençal poetry into modern German.[3]

Schrödinger entered the University of Vienna in 1906, the year that Boltzmann died. The professors who had a decisive influence on him were Boltzmann's students, Fritz Hasenöhrl and Franz Exner. Hasenöhrl delivered a cycle of eight semesters of lectures on theoretical physics, especially Hamiltonian mechanics and the theory of eigenvalue problems in the physics of continua. It was from these lectures, much more than from books, that Schrödinger acquired the foundations for most of his later work. He learned mathematics from Wirtinger and experimental physics from Exner and K. W. F. Kohlrausch. From Exner he also gained that insight into the relation of causality and atomism that became one of the germinal ideas for much of his later thought.

From 1910 to 1914 Schrödinger served as assistant to Exner and wrote papers on magnetism, dielectrics, atmospheric acoustics, radioactivity, X-rays, and Brownian motion. When the war began, he left Vienna to become an artillery officer on the southwest front, incurring no disabilities and little distinction. However, his beloved teacher Hasenöhrl was killed in the conflict. Years later Schrödinger expressed his respect for his teacher and his sense of loss at his death when he avowed that, but for this tragedy, Hasenöhrl might have stood in his place to receive the Nobel Prize in 1933.[4]

In 1918, Schrödinger had hoped to succeed Geitler in theoretical physics at Czernowitz,[5] there to lecture in the tradition of Hasenöhrl

[2] *Ibid.*
[3] In "Erwin Schrödinger zum 60. Geburtstag," *Acta Phys. Austriaca,* 1 (1947), 109.
[4] Autobiographical sketch in *Les Prix Nobel en 1933*, p. 87.
[5] Now Chernovtsy, Ukrainian S.S.R.

and "over and above this" to devote some time to philosophy. In his foreword to his last book, *My View of the World*, Schrödinger recalls that he was "deeply imbued at the time with the writings of Spinoza, Schopenhauer, Mach, Richard Semon, and Richard Avenarius." However, his hopes were not to materialize. "My guardian angel intervened: Czernowitz soon no longer belonged to Austria. So nothing came of it. I had to stick to theoretical physics, and, to my astonishment, something occasionally emerged from it."[6]

Schrödinger returned to Vienna and remained there until 1920. Then in short succession he took a series of posts, each more distinguished than the last. He spent a term at Jena as assistant to Max Wien, a term at Stuttgart as junior professor (*extraordinarius*), and a term as professor (*ordinarius*) at Breslau. Just before going to Jena, he married Annamarie Bertel of Salzburg.

In 1921, at the age of 34, Schrödinger went to Zurich to accept the chair that had been held by Einstein and von Laue. There he found congenial partnership with the mathematician Hermann Weyl and the chemist Peter Debye. An additional attraction of Zurich was its status as a favorite stopping place for journeys to Switzerland and the south. A stream of visitors shared in the lively discussions that were going on in the physics of that day. Walter Heitler, who served as postgraduate fellow in Schrödinger's department, recalled that each Sunday Mrs. Schrödinger arranged a small excursion "which invariably ended in some nice country inn with a glass of wine (or maybe two)."[7]

During the period from the end of the war through his six-year stay in Zurich, Schrödinger's scientific output covered an unusually wide range of subjects. His papers included a few in general relativity, some in probability theory, and a seventy-four page review of dielectric phenomena. A somewhat more extensive effort involved seven papers on three- and four-color theories of vision, a project carried out under the stimulation of Exner and Kohlrausch. It was a piece of physics with a curiously formal similarity to general relativity in that it employed a geometrical representation using a nonlinear metric. Schrödinger frankly described this excursion into optics as an escape from the difficulties of atomic theory.[8]

---

[6] *My View of the World* (Cambridge and New York: Cambridge University Press, 1964), p. viii. Hereafter cited as *MVW*.

[7] "Erwin Schrödinger," *Biographical Memoirs of the Royal Society*, 1961, p. 223.

[8] In "Antrittsrede," *S. B. Preuss. Akad. Wiss.* (1929), p. C.

In spite of this brief detour, Schrödinger's main efforts centered on the puzzles of atomic theory and served as preparation for his great work in wave mechanics. These efforts ranged from a systematic review of the subject of specific heats, through efforts to improve some of the details of the Bohr theory, to studies in the statistical mechanics of gases that followed Einstein in making preliminary use of de Broglie's wave ideas. The crucial papers on wave mechanics were all written in a half-year's burst of activity just before he left Zurich. In contrast to many others who are famous in the history of quantum mechanics,[9] Schrödinger was relatively advanced in age when he came upon his own contribution. At 39 he was still creative enough to make a major discovery in an essentially new line of work. Of this contribution Max Born later wrote, "What is there more sublime in theoretical physics than his first six papers in wave mechanics?"[10]

Schrödinger went to Berlin in 1927 to replace Max Planck upon his retirement from the Chair of Theoretical Physics at the University. In the German capital city a number of institutions—the University, two Hochschulen, the Reichsanstalt, the Kaiser Wilhelm Institute, the Astrophysical Observatory, and several industrial research laboratories—had produced what Schrödinger called "an unparalleled population-density of physicists of the first rank." He found it stimulating and "deeply impressive to see them all collected in the common weekly colloquium."[11] Seldom had there been gathered in one place so many Nobel Prize winners—past and future. In the presence of Einstein, von Laue, Planck, and others, Schrödinger enjoyed the exchange with physicists who were older and more experienced than he. He was later to look back on his stay in Berlin as "scientifically very beautiful and free" (*wissenschaftlich sehr schön und sehr frei*.)[12]

In the years 1926–28, quantum mechanics was brought to completion approximately in the form it has today. In this short period of extraordinarily rich interaction among physicists, several basic principles were discovered which converted a loose union of the matrix mechanics of Heisenberg and the wave mechanics of Schrödinger into the mature

[9] At the time of their first papers in the fields that brought them fame, Einstein was 26 years old, Bohr 28, Pauli 25, Uhlenbeck 25, Goudsmit 23, Heisenberg 24, Dirac 24, and Jordan 23.

[10] "Erwin Schrödinger," *Physik. Blätter* (Feb., 1961), p. 85.

[11] Autobiographical sketch in *Les Prix Nobel en 1933*, p. 87.

[12] *Ibid.*

theory now universally called quantum mechanics. Chief among these principles were the statistical interpretation of Born, the transformation theory of Dirac and Jordan, the uncertainty relation of Heisenberg, and the complementarity concept of Bohr.

Göttingen, Copenhagen, and Cambridge were the principal centers for most of this early work. The leading theoretical physicists in Berlin, Einstein, Planck, von Laue, and Schrödinger, were all reluctant to accept the statistical and dualistic aspects of quantum theory as it had developed in those other centers. Schrödinger's own dissatisfaction with what he was later to call the "makeshift of wave mechanics"[13] led him to explore the foundations of the theory, particularly in its connection with the theory of relativity, and to question the conclusion of Bohr and others that we must give up hope of finding satisfactory conceptual models in the field of atomic physics.[14] He hesitated to push the technical aspects of quantum mechanics further until the necessity for the seemingly unsatisfactory features was clearer to him. He did, however, make a basic and useful discovery in the "trembling motion" (*Zitterbewegung*) undergone by an electron in the Dirac theory.

When Hitler came to power in 1933, physicists of Jewish ancestry began to lose their posts. With his "Aryan" blood and Catholic background, Schrödinger would have been able to continue in Berlin, but he did not want to become politically involved. His sympathies were not with the Nazis, and he chose to leave. "We admired him for it," Max Born wrote, "for it is no little thing to be uprooted in middle age to live in a strange land."[15]

Schrödinger accepted a temporary position at Oxford as Fellow of Magdalen College. Soon after his arrival in England, he received the news that he was to share with Dirac the Nobel Prize in Physics for 1933. His part of the award was of course given for the development of wave mechanics.

In 1936, Schrödinger was offered professorships at Edinburgh and Graz. He chose to return to his homeland; but within two years Hitler annexed Austria, and Schrödinger, already established as an anti-Nazi, decided it would be wise to leave the country while his passport was still valid. He was encouraged in his decision by a message from Eamon de

---

[13] *Science and Humanism* (Cambridge: Cambridge University Press, 1951), p. 39. Cited hereafter as *SH*.
[14] See Ch. IV, sec. 8 below.
[15] *Op. cit.*, p. 86.

Valera, the President of the Irish Republic, who saw a place for him in the Institute for Advanced Studies which he dreamed of some day founding in Dublin. Keeping discretely silent about their plans, Professor and Mrs. Schrödinger packed the belongings they could fit into three suitcases, left their home, car, and other possessions behind them, and fled to Rome. There, at the age of 51, without either a post or a right to pension, Schrödinger sought refuge and assistance as a member of the Pontifical Academy.

Shortly after his arrival in Rome, Schrödinger was called to Geneva where de Valera was serving as President of the 1938 meeting of the Assembly of the League of Nations. Between sessions of the Assembly, the two men discussed the possibility of establishing an institute which could revive and strengthen Ireland's place in the international community of mathematics and theoretical physics. De Valera, himself a mathematician, saw the special appeal of a school of theoretical physics which would be devoted solely to the advancement of learning and which would center on the study of "that branch of science in which you want no elaborate equipment, in which all you want is an adequate library, the brains and the men, and just paper."[16]

It was not until 1940 that the Irish government officially established the Dublin Institute for Advanced Studies and that Erwin Schrödinger was appointed Director of the School of Theoretical Physics. In the interim, he went first to Belgium under the sponsorship of the Fondation Francqui in Brussels. At the outbreak of war in the fall of 1939, arrangements were made for the Schrödingers to come to Ireland. The bill proposing the establishment of the Institute had been presented to the Dáil Éireann the previous summer, but pending its passage and final plans for the new center, Professor Schrödinger taught an informal course of elementary lectures for undergraduates in University College, Dublin, and conducted a series of advanced formal lectures on quantum theory at the Royal Irish Academy.

In 1941 the Institute formally opened with a symposium on meson theory. For Erwin Schrödinger, the event marked the beginning of a more settled period, the longest sojourn of his academic career. Thirring describes his professorship as "that ideal post that a researcher can only wish for himself: complete freedom of teaching and research without any

[16] *Fifteen Year Report of the School of Theoretical Physics, Dublin Institute for Advanced Studies, 29 October 1940 to 31 March 1955* (Dublin: Dublin Institute for Advanced Studies, 1961), p. vii.

specific teaching obligations, similar to that professorship at the Berlin Academy of Science that first Van 't Hoff and later Einstein held and which was jokingly referred to in circles of specialists as the 'Place of the Honored Genie.'"[17]

Walter Heitler, who joined the Institute at its opening, recalls the lovely eighteenth-century Georgian building on Merrion Square in Old Dublin, "very suitable and comfortable for quiet work unburdened by mass lecturing and the modern curse of the scientists—administration."[18] Within a few minutes' walk of the Institute are clustered a number of learned institutions: Trinity College, University College, Dublin, and the Royal Irish Academy, formerly presided over by the great Sir William Hamilton whose formulation of mechanics played a central role in Schrödinger's own work.

Within the new Institute itself the spirit was excellent. A varied and lively community developed, bringing together advanced students and professors and lecturers from both the nearby universities. For the summers, Schrödinger planned special informal colloquia to discuss pertinent questions of physics. Max Born recalls coming from Edinburgh for those "exciting and amusing gatherings in which the former mathematician and current minister-president of the Irish Republic normally took part."[19]

In the congenial surroundings of the Institute Schrödinger worked actively for a period of 15 years. Most of his papers of this period were in the area of space-time structure and unified field theory. He also worked on meson fields and nonlinear electrodynamics, and continued his interest in quantum mechanics and statistics. Approximately half of his philosophical and popular writings were composed during this period.

As senior professor, Schrödinger had the pleasant responsibility of periodically giving a series of public lectures. A gifted popular interpreter, he stimulated his audiences by his clarity, wit, and profundity. His public lectures were models of lucid exposition, bringing together philosophical and scientific concerns in language the layman could understand. Four of his books (*What is Life?*, *Nature and the Greeks*, *Science and Humanism*, *Mind and Matter*) had their genesis in such public lecture series.

[17] "Erwin Schrödinger zum 60. Geburtstag," *Acta Phys. Austriaca*, 1 (1947), p. 108.
[18] "Erwin Schrödinger," *Biographical Memoirs of the Royal Society*, 1961, p. 224.
[19] *Loc. cit.*

In 1956, toward the end of Schrödinger's stay in Dublin, bronchitis and asthma set in, seriously limiting his productivity. His friend Hans Thirring arranged a special chair for him as Professor Emeritus of Theoretical Physics at the University of Vienna, and Schrödinger returned once again to his homeland. His only two publications written during these last years in Vienna represented further development of his two principal philosophical interests: an article on the interpretation of quantum mechanics, "Might Perhaps Energy Be a Merely Statistical Concept?" and an article on the problem of nature and the self, "What is Real?" He spent his summers in his favorite village of Alpach in the Tirol, and it was there that he was buried when he finally succumbed to prolonged illness on January 4, 1961.

No simple account of the life and work of Erwin Schrödinger can do justice to the complexity and vigor of his personality. His interests were wide-ranging, his insights penetrating. In a memorial essay on his friend, Max Born expressed his own reluctance "to draw a portrait of this glittering, many-sided man,"[20] this *uomo universale* who was equally at home in the realms of science and the classics, who loved poetry and wrote verse of his own, who was widely acquainted with modern and classical art, who tried his hand at sculpture, and who quoted the Greek philosophers as he lectured on problems of theoretical physics. "The breadth of his knowledge was as marvelous as the acuity and heuristic power of his thought," Born remarked.[21]

Even in his student days at the University of Vienna, Schrödinger made a deep impression on his fellows. Hans Thirring recalls the day of his own first encounter. He was then a neophyte, sitting in the library of the mathematics seminar. A blond student came into the room, and Thirring's neighbor poked him, saying, "Das ist der *Schrödinger*." "I had never heard the name before," Thirring writes, "but the respect with which it was said and the way my colleague looked at him made a great impression on me. In that first meeting I arrived at a conviction that grew stronger with the course of years: that one is somebody special."[22]

In a lifetime of intense scientific productivity Schrödinger more than fulfilled the expectations of his friends. In addition to ten books in the areas of physics and philosophy and a volume of poetry, Schrödinger

[20] *Ibid.*
[21] *Ibid.*
[22] *Op. cit.*, p. 106.

wrote more than 150 papers.[23] An outline of the areas of physics to which he contributed gives some indication of the scope of his interests:

I. *Statistical Mechanics*

    A. Statistical thermodynamics, gas theory, etc.
    B. Probability theory and applications
    C. Magnetism
    D. Brownian motion
    E. Dielectrics
    F. Specific heats

II. *Quantum Mechanics*

    A. Spectroscopy
    B. Wave mechanics
    C. Factorization
    D. Dirac theory
    E. Meson theory
    F. Quantum theory of measurement
    G. Interpretation of quantum theory

III. *Space-Time Structure*

    A. General relativity
    B. Affine connections
    C. Unified field theory
    D. Cosmology
    E. Interplanetary fields

IV. *Selections from the Rest of Physics*

    A. Radioactivity and cosmic rays
    B. Acoustics
    C. Surface tension
    D. Classical dynamics
    E. X-ray interference
    F. Color vision and pigments
    G. Electrodynamics and optics
    H. Superconductivity

[23] A full listing of all Schrödinger's papers for which I could find reference is given in the Bibliography. The term "book" excludes collections of previously published papers.

Schrödinger's philosophical writings are also wide-ranging, if more difficult to classify exactly. While most of his writings overlap several topics, an approximate classification is possible:

I. *Philosophy of Science*
   A. Basis for acceptance of laws and theories
   B. Spirit and motivation of science
   C. Science and the cultural milieu
   D. History of science

II. *The Scientific World View*
   A. Determinism and indeterminism
   B. The nature of the physical world

III. *Life and the Self*
   A. Biology and physics
   B. Mind and matter

In evaluating his scientific output at the time of his Nobel address, Schrödinger commented that in his work, as in his life, he never followed "a strong line, a program that would provide direction over a long period of time." He continued, "Although I can work with others only poorly ... my work is nevertheless not wholly self-sufficient, as my interest in a question is always derived from the fact that others are interested in it. My word is seldom the first, but often the second, and is awakened through the wish to contradict or to set aright; however, the obvious continuation may later show itself as more important than the contradiction which served as a point of departure."[24]

The printed page only records the outcome of these efforts to reconstruct or to set aright—there must have been countless lively discussions before and after. Schrödinger liked to go to the heart of a question; often the discovery that someone else was wrong served as the opening to a new level of profundity, a new creative insight. True to his Viennese heritage, his critical spirit flourished in convivial relationships—friendship was not broken by disagreements, rather, disagreements and arguments were part of a common search for the truth. Max Born remembers Schrödinger's characteristic combination of warm, charming friendship and sharp, almost unpleasant, argumentativeness. He and

[24] My translation from "Erwin Schrödinger," Autobiographical sketch in *Les Prix Nobel en 1933*, pp. 87–88.

Born carried on a continual battle of ideas over the interpretation of quantum mechanics, yet the familiar "du" was always used between them. Even after Schrödinger had teasingly scolded Born for his insistence on the Copenhagen view of quantum mechanics,[25] no resentment lingered on to darken the relationship.

Although Schrödinger's professional life involved a constant and lively interchange of ideas with others, his actual work was done almost entirely alone. Only ten of his papers bear other authors' names. According to his own account he had difficulty working with students,[26] and he rarely accepted research students to work with him.[27]

In Schrödinger's view, the communal aspects of science go far beyond the conviviality typified by his relations with colleagues, if not with students.

The entire cultural milieu, he believed, is of major importance in determining the particular directions taken in science and the kinds of theories acknowledged to be valid clues to truth. In "Is Science a Fashion of the Times?" he wrote:

> Our civilization forms an organic whole. Those fortunate individuals who can devote their lives to the profession of scientific research are not merely botanists or physicists or chemists, as the case may be. They are men and they are children of their age. The scientist cannot shuffle off his mundane coil when he enters his laboratory or ascends the rostrum in his lecture hall. In the morning his leading interest in class or in the laboratory may be his research; but what was he doing the afternoon and evening before? He attends public meetings just as others do or he reads about them in the press. He cannot and does not wish to escape discussion of the mass of ideas that are constantly thronging in the foreground of public interest, especially in our day. Some scientists are lovers of music, some read novels and poetry, some frequent theaters. Some will be interested in painting and sculpture. And if any one should believe that he could really escape the influence of the cinema, because he does not care for it, he is surely mistaken. For he cannot even walk along the street without paying attention to the pictures of cinema stars and advertisement tableaux. In short, we are all members of our cultural environment.[28]

---

[25] "Du, Maxel, du weisst, ich hab' dich lieb, und daran kann nichts etwas ändern. Aber ich habe das Bedürfnis, Dir mal gründlich den Kopf zu waschen." M. Born, *op. cit.*, p. 85.

[26] Autobiographical sketch in *Les Prix Nobel en 1933*, p. 87.

[27] W. Heitler, *op. cit.*, p. 225.

[28] In *Science Theory and Man* (New York: Dover Publications, Inc., 1957, and London: Allen and Unwin, 1958), pp. 98–99. Hereafter cited as *STM*.

Observing the world around him, Schrödinger saw a series of contemporary trends which he believed to be shared by science, the arts, politics, and social organization: the desire for change and for freedom from authority, for simplicity and purposefulness in the arts and the crafts, and the interest in relativity and invariance.

The period of Schrödinger's early life was the end of an era in European civilization—the "Golden Age of Security," as Stefan Zweig called it. Classical ideals were glorified; the wisdom of old men was preferred to the dynamic energy of the young. New ideas were accepted reluctantly, until the political events of 1914 upset the old order and introduced everywhere a ferment of social and political change.

In physics, too, Schrödinger's youth came at the end of an era—that which we now call the classical period. In the late nineteenth century Maxwell's theory of the electromagnetic field had seemed to complete the structure of Newtonian physics, leaving only the pursuit of the "next decimal place" to future research. Max Planck was advised in 1875 to study classics because all the important discoveries had already been made. Yet the years between Schrödinger's birth and maturity also saw the discoveries of electrons, X-rays, radioactivity, isotopes, the quantum ideas for radiation and photoelectricity, and relativity. Radical changes in the outlook of physics became necessary, and entirely new areas of research were to open up.

The burning problems of this new era in physics can be summarized by two general questions: What indeed are the properties of the atomic and subatomic entities for which the new experimental techniques provided a steady stream of clues? How could the over-all structure of physics, seemingly so perfected at the end of the previous century, be modified and developed to include the peculiar properties of these atomic entities?

Several underlying strands of thought run through the diversity of Schrödinger's own approaches to these two great issues. In his foreword to *What is Life? and Other Scientific Essays*, he remarks, "Indeed, what provides a certain unity to the whole is that the author has in the course of the years formed a small number of definite ways of thought that are very relevant to him and to which he therefore returns again and again on various occasions."[29]

---

[29] *What is Life? and Other Scientific Essays* (Garden City, New York: Doubleday Anchor Books, 1956). Cited hereafter as *WIL*.

Among these lines of thought are those involving the statistical explanation of macroscopic phenomena in terms of atomism, wave mechanics itself, and the interpretation of wave mechanics as an approach to a clear and comprehensible form of quantum theory. All of these areas relate to problems of freedom and causality, as well as to problems of the relation of the observer to the world observed, and thus have a direct connection with his philosophical interest. These lines of thought—statistics, atomism, wave mechanics and its interpretation, nature and the self—will be our concern.

In his search for truth Schrödinger felt free to cross the boundaries of traditional subject matter and to ask his own questions of nature in new ways. He looked at scientific effort as "part of man's endeavor to grasp the human situation."[30] He deplored the kind of narrow specialization which serves as an end in itself, for he saw the value of science "only in its synthesis with all the rest of knowledge and only as it really contributes to this synthesis something toward answering the demand, '$\tau\acute{\iota}\nu\epsilon\varsigma$ $\delta\grave{\epsilon}$ $\acute{\eta}\mu\epsilon\hat{\iota}\varsigma$' (Who are we?)."[31]

In the introductory chapter of *Nature and the Greeks* Schrödinger wrote with feeling about the period of "alluring primeval unity," when there was no wall to separate the paths of reason and the heart. In that early time "there was no limitation as to the subjects on which a learned man would be allowed by other learned men to give his opinion. It was still agreed that the true subject was essentially one, and that important conclusions reached about any part of it could, and as a rule would, bear on almost every other part."[32]

Schrödinger continued, drawing from antiquity a picture of teacher and student engaged in a discussion of central questions of nature and the self:

> To put it dramatically: one can imagine a scholar of the young School of Athens paying a holiday visit to Abdera (with due caution to keep it secret from his Master), and on being received by the wise, far-travelled and world-famous old gentleman Democritus, asking him questions on the atoms, on the shape of the earth, on moral conduct, God, and the immortality of the soul—without being repudiated on any of these points. Can you easily

[30] Preface to *SH*, page unnumbered.
[31] *SH*, p. 5; reprinted in *WIL*, p. 113.
[32] *Nature and the Greeks* (Cambridge: Cambridge University Press, 1954), p. 12; hereafter cited as *NG*; *WIL*, p. 97.

imagine such a motley conversation between a student and a teacher in our days? Yet, in all probability, quite a few young people have a similar—we should say quaint—collection of inquiries on their minds and would like to discuss all of them with the one person of their confidence.[33]

Schrödinger would have been the last person to compare himself to the universal teacher he described. Yet anyone who has explored the variety and depth of his work will find in this account an apt model for his genius.

[33] *NG*, pp. 12–13; *WIL*; p. 98.

Chapter II

The Heritage of Boltzmann

1. THE STATISTICAL AND ATOMISTIC LINES OF THOUGHT

In speaking of the great Boltzmann, Schrödinger declared, "His line of thought may be called my first love in science. No other has ever thus enraptured me or will ever do so again."[1] Boltzmann's line of thought, the statistical basis of thermodynamics,[2] runs through many of Schrödinger's papers, not as a single thread but as a growing vine with many offshoots into physics and philosophy.

Statistical methods and the calculus of probability were introduced into various branches of science in the last century. These methods are useful both for problems involving random errors and uncontrolled extraneous influences and for situations of great complexity in which information on all the elements, e.g., the positions and velocities of every molecule, cannot possibly be treated in detail. Boltzmann's contribution to statistics involved deeper considerations than those implied in these pragmatic questions, however. He showed that the results obtained by statistical methods involving a deliberate suppression of quantitative details are not only more interesting than a full treatment of detail could be, but, more important, they bring to light new variables and new significance in any physical situation to which they are applied.[3]

Schrödinger ranked Boltzmann's development of the statistical–

---

[1] *S. B. Preuss. Akad. Wiss.* (1929), pp. C–CII; reprinted in *STM*, pp. xii–xviii.

[2] J. Willard Gibbs contributed equally with Boltzmann to the development of statistical mechanics and thermodynamics; his name is not emphasized here because his influence on Schrödinger was not direct, although of course Schrödinger made use of Gibbs's approach along with Boltzmann's.

[3] See E. Schrödinger, *Nature*, **153** (1944), 704–705.

mechanical theory of heat as one of the two leading ideas of nineteenth-century natural science, along with Darwinism.[4] Schrödinger's own work in the statistical area started with attempts to solve problems of the solid state of matter—magnetism, dielectric behavior, and specific heats. His interest led him to treatment of the Brownian movement, to the theory of gases, and to questions of probability theory. His study of gases provided substantial clues to the later work in wave mechanics and to the consideration of foundation questions in statistical mechanics itself.

The value of applying the statistical method to problems of the human community was stressed by Schrödinger in one of his popular writings, "Physical Science and the Temper of the Age."[5] The prudent and systematic ignoring of details leads to laws of a new kind that furnish new information concerning human affairs, just as the deductions of astronomy concerning the size and shape of the galaxy are derived by using data on the average number of stars of different magnitudes, ignoring details of the individual characteristics of particular stars. Schrödinger called this statistical method "a dominant feature of our epoch and an important instrument of progress in almost every sphere of public life."[6]

The central proposition of the heritage of Boltzmann is that the universality of the Second Law of Thermodynamics is a consequence for macroscopic physics of the very existence of atoms. Franz Exner carried the statistical point of view further and raised the question whether all physics does not have a statistical nature as a result of its atomic foundations. These profound questions thoroughly embedded the atomistic line of thought in the inheritance Schrödinger had received from his teachers. They led to his concern with indeterminacy and the wave nature of atoms, and to his interest in Greek origins of the concept of atomism. Some of his most profound speculations were based on the problem of the direction of time as seen in statistical mechanics, and on that of the self as seen in the causal and statistical aspects of the atomic nature of things.

2. STATISTICAL PAPERS, EARLY AND LATE

A major proportion of Schrödinger's early papers was devoted to applications of statistical mechanics. In an article published in the *Wiener*

---

[4] "Der Geist der Naturwissenschaft," published in English as "The Spirit of Science" in *WIL*, p. 235.

[5] *STM*, pp. 106–132.

[6] *Ibid.*, p. 130.

Berichte in 1912, he made an attempt to explain diamagnetism using the Lorentz electron theory and the Maxwell–Boltzmann distribution law.[7] The results disagreed rather drastically with experiment, being of the right order of magnitude for only one element (Bismuth) of the four he compared. The statistical methods were elementary and approximate; they did not have the degree of generality of Bohr's proof that classical methods always give a strictly zero result.[8]

In the same volume of the *Wiener Berichte*, we find a long article on the solid state of matter,[9] in which Schrödinger attempted to use the concept of a permanent electric dipole to account for the phenomena of melting and of piezo- and pyro-electricity. He used the same concept a few months later to deal with anomalous electric dispersion,[10] following work of Debye that was based on Einstein's theory of Brownian motion.[11] Schrödinger proposed experiments which he thought might sort out dipole interactions from resonance effects. Needless to say, these calculations, which Schrödinger had made without benefit of modern quantum mechanics, have long since lost most of their significance.

However, quantum theory in its older formulation did provide a basis for comprehending the specific heats of solids, and Schrödinger came back to solid state physics in 1919 with a five-part review paper on this subject.[12] Here he reviewed extensively both experiment and theory, provided much data and many references, and concluded with the assertion that quantum theory had been largely successful, but that more remained to be done, for instance with the specific heat of electrons in metals.

In 1921, Born and Brody[13] used the Bohr theory to calculate a correction term, linear in temperature, to the well-known law of Dulong and Petit for the specific heats of solids. Schrödinger rederived this result in a

[7] *S. B. Akad. Wiss. Wien*, Abt. 2a, **121** (1912), 1305–1328.

[8] See J. H. Van Vleck, *The Theory of Electric and Magnetic Susceptibilities* (Oxford: Clarendon Press, 1932), pp. 101–104. Bohr's work was in his dissertation (Copenhagen, 1911).

[9] *S. B. Akad. Wiss. Wien*, Abt. 2a, **121** (1912), 1937–1972.

[10] *Verhandl. deut. physik. Ges.*, **15** (1913), 1167–1172.

[11] P. Debye, *Ann. Physik*, **39** (1912), 789–839; A. Einstein, *Ann. Physik*, **17** (1905), 549–560, **19** (1906), 371–381, and **22** (1907), 569–572.

[12] *Physik. Z.*, **20** (1919), 420–428, 450–455, 474–480, 497–503, 523–526. This work is mentioned in F. K. Richtmyer, *Introduction to Modern Physics* (1st ed.; New York: McGraw-Hill, 1928), p. 272; (3rd ed.; E. H. Kennard, co-author; New York: McGraw-Hill, 1942), pp. 454–456.

[13] M. Born and E. Brody, *Z. Physik*, **6** (1921), 132–139 and 140–152.

simple way without use of the Bohr theory, but then extended the Bohr-type calculations of Born and Brody by using a form of time-dependent perturbation theory similar to that later used in wave mechanics.[14] His work on specific heats culminated in a clear, competent, and extensive article in the Geiger–Scheel *Handbuch der Physik* on the theory of specific heats in gases and solids.[15] In this article, he focused attention on troubles of the old quantum theory.

Schrödinger developed a related study of considerable value for solid-state theory, even without the use of quantization, on consideration of a single line of elastically-coupled atoms. Born and von Kármán[16] had developed a theory of a three-dimensional crystal lattice, using an analysis into harmonic oscillations (Fourier analysis). Schrödinger was able to extend this analysis in the one-dimensional example in ways that were not easy or even possible in the three-dimensional model. His principal application concerned the effect of random heat motion on the broadening of the spots or maxima in the interference patterns produced when X-rays traverse crystals.[17] This calculation involved the statistical assumption that the observation time is sufficiently long for all configurations of the several atoms to appear in proportion to their probabilities, "a restriction," said Schrödinger, "that since Boltzmann all natural laws must be subjected to."[18] As Born later pointed out,[19] Schrödinger had obtained with this rigorous but one-dimensional calculation the correct result in the classical (high temperature) region, and thus made a small and temporary, but nevertheless important, contribution to this special field. In another article Schrödinger showed that the results were independent of the boundary conditions and involved chiefly those pairs of atoms which are close together.[20]

A more general development of this same example was to show in a detailed way how to pass from the discrete atomic nature of the system

---

[14] *Z. Physik*, **11** (1922), 170–176.

[15] "Spezifische Wärme (theoretischer Teil)," *Handbuch der Physik*, ed. H. Geiger and K. Scheel (Berlin: Julius Springer, 1926), **10**, 275–320.

[16] M. Born and Th. von Kármán, *Physik. Z.*, **13** (1912), 297–309; **14** (1913), 15–19, and 65–71.

[17] *Physik. Z.*, **15** (1914), 79–86.

[18] *Ibid.*

[19] *Reports on Progress in Physics*, **9** (1942–3), 294–296. See also comments of P. P. Ewald, *Handbuch der Physik*, ed. H. Geiger and K. Scheel (2nd ed.; Berlin: Julius Springer, 1933), **4**, 310.

[20] *Physik. Z.*, **15**, (1914), 497–503.

to the continuum (an idealized string or rod). The harmonic analysis method tends to conceal these details; Schrödinger instead cleverly exploited the properties of Bessel functions, especially recursion relations between functions with successive indices and sums with respect to the index.[21] His method makes it possible to deal with the development of motion in a chain of particles when just one is initially disturbed and to show that in passing to the limit of infinitely many infinitesimally spaced atoms, initial conditions must be used that do not consist of the displacement of one atom, but rather of a group that in their initial displacements already approximate a smooth, continuous function. Schrödinger, in fact, derived the wave equation for a rod or string from these considerations. He asserted that thermal resistivity can be derived in this way from the fact of atomicity, but as MacDonald made clear in a reference to this work, the chief "classical" reason for thermal resistivity is the anharmonicity of the lattice vibrations.[22]

Statistical mechanics of Boltzmann's type is applied chiefly to events where very large numbers are involved, as in the molecular theory of gases. Similar probability calculations may also be applied to cases involving far fewer events, as in the displacements of a group of dust particles or oil drops undergoing Brownian motion. In the latter case, quantities more involved than mean values can be derived using the ordinary ideas of probability theory. One such is the distribution in first-passage times, i.e., the times at which any one of a set of randomly moving particles first crosses a given line. This problem is relevant to measurements of the electronic charge from observations of the rise and fall of microscopic particles under the action of an electric field.

At the time when Millikan's famous oil-drop experiments were being performed, a controversy raged as to whether F. Ehrenhaft and his collaborators in Vienna had actually found values for the charge on the electron that were quite small fractions of Millikan's fairly well established result for this indivisible unit of electricity.[23] Schrödinger's ability to make a basic contribution without getting himself directly involved in

[21] *Ann. Physik.*, **44** (1914), 916–934; *S. B. Akad. Wiss. Wien.*, Abt. 2a, **123** (1914), 1679–1696.
[22] D. K. C. MacDonald, *Proceedings of the International Symposium on Transport Processes in Statistical Mechanics* (New York: Interscience, 1958), pp. 63–72.
[23] For R. A. Millikan's results and his own view (and careful analysis) of Ehrenhaft's work, see his book, *The Electron* (1st ed.; Chicago: Univ. of Chicago Press, 1917). Many references to Ehrenhaft's work are given there. See also R. Bär, *Naturwissenschaften*, **10** (1922), 344–350.

the controversy was shown in his paper on Brownian motion, where he offered a clear and accurate calculation of the first-passage-time problem.[24] He employed here the delightful pedagogical technique he so often used later, that of explaining and disposing of several attractive but erroneous ways of handling the problem before presenting the correct, if lengthy, method. He also made a penetrating observation on the fallacy of using the smallness of fluctuations at the end of a cumulative series as a criterion for the smallness of the error of a result calculated from the entire series. Schrödinger's results were not, in fact, used to settle the controversy (Millikan's techniques and controls were simply far superior to those of Ehrenhaft), but the work remains valuable as another small contribution to a field largely developed by others. Kennard, for instance, quoted from it, reproducing the derivation.[25]

The theory of Brownian motion which Einstein developed and which Schrödinger applied to the above problem involves the assumption of a viscous force acting on the particle to slow it down.[26] Rubin has recently made an interesting extension of Schrödinger's work on the dynamics of a line of elastically-coupled particles.[27] By assuming one of the particles to have a mass M much larger than the common value m for all the others, this author derives a formula for Brownian motion without having to make a special assumption about viscosity.

Underlying the theory of Brownian motion and of many other random processes is the so-called Fokker–Planck diffusion equation,[28] derived from a differential-integral equation of Boltzmann's type by expanding the unknown function in the integrand as a Taylor's series in the independent variable. Referring to experiments concerning fluctuations in the emission of alpha and beta particles from radioactive sources,[29] Schrödinger applied a very general form of the Fokker–Planck equation to some of the dynamical problems involved in electrometer measurements, particularly

[24] *Physik. Z.*, **16** (1915), 289–295.

[25] E. H. Kennard, *Kinetic Theory of Gases* (New York: McGraw-Hill, 1938), pp. 288–290.

[26] See Einstein, *op. cit.*

[27] R. J. Rubin, *Proceedings of the International Symposium on Transport Processes in Statistical Mechanics* (New York: Interscience, 1958), pp. 155–160; see ref. 21.

[28] A. D. Fokker, *Ann. Physik*, **43** (1914), 810–820; M. Planck, *S. B. Preuss. Akad. Wiss.* (1917), 324–341. See also the second paper of ref. 11.

[29] The statistics of radioactivity was first discussed by E. von Schweidler, *Premier Congrès International de Radiation*, Liège, 1905 (Brussels: Severegns, 1906), p. 498.

in the fluctuations of the movement of a pointer in a given time or of the time taken for a given pointer displacement.[30] As usual, these papers contain clear expository material, in this case on the diffusion equation and the theory of errors.[31] The experimental work he referred to was carried out at the Institut für Radiumforschung of the University of Vienna, where Schrödinger had himself collaborated with K. W. F. Kohlrausch some years earlier in an experiment on soft secondary electrons produced by gamma rays in various absorbers.[32]

Six papers of the period from 1940 to 1951 show Schrödinger's continuing interest in statistical methods. With T. S. Broderick,[33] he published a general paper on Boolean algebra and probability theory, following up an earlier paper of Broderick's[34] using symbolic multiplication. The essence of this paper is the use of an isomorphism between certain sets of classes and the elements of any Boolean algebra. Application is made to an extension of the first-passage-time problem, namely, the problem of the first appearance in a random series of a set of at least one each of a finite number of possible distinct events.

Pius Servien remarked in the preface to his 1942 book on probability theory that the concept of probability is the central concept of modern physics and yet its development is still clouded with difficulties.[35] The challenge of this remark led Schrödinger to extend his specific work in two papers on the foundations of probability, taking only the product rule, or a normalization of a measure of likelihood, as the basic axiom, in place of a frequency definition.[36]

In 1944, L. Jánossy[37] made a calculation of the rate of accidental coincidences between n Geiger counters exposed to cosmic rays; Schrödinger calculated the second approximation.[38] Another counter problem connected with cosmic rays was suggested by C. B. H. McCusker and

---

[30] *S. B. Akad. Wiss. Wien.*, Abt. 2a, **127** (1918), 237–262, and **128** (1919), 177–237.

[31] K. W. F. Kohlrausch refers to this work as an important and very general treatment of fluctuation phenomena in electrometer experiments. Cf. W. Wien and F. Harms, eds., *Handbuch der Experimental Physik* (Leipzig, 1928), XV, 793–795.

[32] *S. B. Akad. Wiss. Wien.*, Abt. 2a, **123** (1914), 1319–1367.

[33] *Proc. R. Irish Acad.*, **46**A (1940), 103–112.

[34] *Proc. R. Irish Acad.*, **44**A (1937), 19–28.

[35] P. Servien [Coculesco], *Base Physique et base mathématique de la théorie des probabilités: vers une nouvelle forme de la théorie* (Paris: Hermann, 1942).

[36] *Proc. R. Irish Acad.*, **51**A (1947), 51–66 and 141–150.

[37] *Nature*, **153** (1944), 165.

[38] *Nature*, **153** (1944), 592–593, with adjacent reply by L. Jánossy.

solved by Schrödinger in 1951, namely, the probability that m out of a set of r counters are each hit by one of a set of n rays.[39] The sixth paper (1945) was an example of probability calculus connected with elementary nuclear chain-reaction theory, evidently inspired by the success of the first atomic bombs, on the probability of cessation of such a reaction.[40]

3. THE STATISTICAL THEORY OF GASES

Four papers on the theory of gases deserve special mention, for they represent Schrödinger's involvement in a long-standing controversy that was only resolved by the further development of quantum theory, and they form a partial introduction to his great work, the invention of wave mechanics.

The controversy had to do with the proper expression for the entropy S of a gas in terms of the enumeration of the different possible states of molecular motion and the probabilities of their occurrence. One source of the difficulty was the development and acceptance of Nernst's heat theorem, and another was the so-called Gibbs paradox, related to the failure of an otherwise well-established formula for entropy to provide the proper additivity characteristics for mixtures of gases.[41]

One form of Nernst's heat theorem[42] states that the work done in expanding any system will vanish when performed at absolute zero. Applied to gases, this means that the perfect gas law, $PV = nRT$, must fail for a gas cooled down to $T = 0$. T must disappear from the equation of state because, according to Schrödinger, "there are no entropy transactions."[43] Quite aside from the possibility of condensation, the Nernst theorem predicts the occurrence of a kind of degeneration (*Gasentartung*). Theoretical and experimental efforts were made to investigate this behavior. The theoretical efforts implied the existence of a characteristic temperature Θ which signified the onset of such behavior as the actual temperature was lowered past this value. Values of Θ for

---

[39] E. Schrödinger, *Proc. Phys. Soc.* A, **64** (1951), 1040–1041.

[40] *Proc. R. Irish Acad.*, **51A** (1945), 1–8. See the use of this calculation by W. Feller: *An Introduction to Probability Theory and Its Applications* (New York: Wiley, 1950), pp. 223–224.

[41] J. Willard Gibbs, *Scientific Papers* (New York: Longmans, Green, 1906), I, 165–168.

[42] W. Nernst, *Die theoretischen und experimentellen Grundlagen des neuen Wärmesatzes* (Halle: W. Knappes, 1918).

[43] *Statistical Thermodynamics* (Cambridge: Cambridge University Press, 1946 and 1952), p. 71.

different theories ranged all the way from an (at the time) unobservable $10^{-4}°$K to the experimentally false value of room temperature.

The method of Boltzmann and Gibbs involves calculating the properties of gases from an entropy function, which is based on the counting of equally-probable states of molecular agitation. If N particles (in the classical sense) can each have states of motion which can be labeled 1, 2, 3, ..., the number of different ways in which there can be n_1 in state 1, n_2 in state 2, and so forth, is

$$W = \frac{N!}{n_1! \, n_2! \, n_3! \cdots}$$

as can be shown by fairly elementary combinatorial analysis. (We must have, of course, $n_1 + n_2 + n_3 + \cdots = N$.) Boltzmann's original definition of entropy was that, letting W_{max} signify the maximum value that W can have among the various possibilities, $S = k \log_e W_{max}$. If there is an enormous number of particles, all but a very tiny fraction of the possible arrangements give almost exactly the maximum value of W.

Now, from this definition one can derive numerous properties of a volume V of gas containing N particles which agree with observations.[44] But, if one combines two similar volumes V, getting a volume $2V$ with $2N$ particles, the entropy does not double as expected. The paradox of Gibbs is contained in the fact that while the mixing of two different gases is correctly given by this theory, the mixing of two amounts of the same gas gives absurd results.[45] (A purely thermodynamic way out of the difficulty was proposed by Schrödinger himself in terms of a *Gedankenexperiment* using a gravitational field.[46] While illustrating the author's ability to pursue sidelines constructively, it does not fit directly into the stream of statistical thought we are pursuing in this chapter.)

It was seen by many physicists that correct results would be obtained if the $N!$ were removed from the formula for W.[47] But there was doubt whether any sound theoretical reason could be found for the consequent subtraction of $k \log_e N!$ from the entropy. The resolution of both of these problems in quantum theory, as we shall see, involves the indistinguishability of individual molecules.

Since the ideal gas law $PV = nRT$ is derivable from consideration of

[44] *Ibid.*, Ch. I.
[45] *Ibid.*, Ch. VIII.
[46] *Z. Physik*, **5** (1921), 163–166.
[47] L. Nordheim, *Z. Physik*, **27** (1924), 65–73.

the translational molecular motion alone, without reference to rotation and vibration but with the assumption of a classically-allowable continuous range of energies, it was natural to approach the degeneration problem by applying quantum rules to the translational motion. The older quantum theory seemed to apply (even if in a rather patchwork fashion) to the rotational motion.[48] In fact, Schrödinger contributed to this patchwork in discussing the half unit of electron angular momentum that band-spectrum theory seemed to require for molecular hydrogen,[49] but its application to translation was quite uncertain.

Schrödinger's first paper on gas theory dealt with the question of which characteristic length should be used for the quantization rule and gave a not very convincing argument for using the mean free path; the article made reference to the $N!$ problem without solving it.[50] The second, a general discussion on the definition of S for ideal gases, constituted part of a three-fold discussion with Einstein and Planck[51] which was published in the *Berliner Berichte*. Schrödinger tried to show that the process of establishing the subtraction of $k \log_e N!$ on theoretical grounds, e.g., on grounds that the individuality of molecules has been taken too seriously in the Boltzmann formulation, leads to the Einstein–Bose form[52] of statistics, in radical contrast to the Boltzmann–Gibbs form. However, the idea of treating the entire gas as a single system to be quantized did not at that time seem possible. The new statistics left in the dark the type of interaction between molecules that could make them indistinguishable. Schrödinger concluded that the key to the difficulty possibly was to be found in his previous paper, in which collisions and the mean free path were considered.

The third article[53] was based on a private communication from Einstein suggesting that the allowed energy levels for a gas of N particles should be chosen so as to put one level in each phase cell of volume

---

[48] F. Reiche, *The Quantum Theory*, trans. H. S. Hatfield and H. L. Brose (New York: Dutton, 1930), pp. 68–80; German ed., *Die Quantentheorie* (Berlin: Springer, 1922).

[49] *Z. Physik.*, **30** (1924), 341–349.

[50] *Physik. Z.*, **25** (1924), 41–45.

[51] *S. B. Preuss. Akad. Wiss.* (1925), 434–441; A. Einstein, *S. B. Preuss. Akad. Wiss.* (1924), 261–267, and (1925) 18–25; M. Planck, *S. B. Preuss. Akad. Wiss.* (1925), 49–57 and 442–451.

[52] A. Einstein, *S. B. Preuss. Akad. Wiss.* (1924), 261–267 and (1925) 18–25; [S. N.] Bose, *Z. Physik*, **26** (1924), 178–181.

[53] *S. B. Preuss. Akad. Wiss.* (1926), 23–36.

$N! \, h^{3N}$. This seemed to be the only way to treat a body of gas as a whole and still to maintain the quasi-ergodic hypothesis. The results concerning degeneracy were unclear and, because of the new approach, very difficult to compare with the earlier mean-free-path approach.

In the fourth article,[54] Schrödinger took seriously the de Broglie hypothesis of matter-waves associated with every particle.[55] This assumption allowed him to treat the gas as a set of wavelike oscillations, using de Broglie's formulas, and to derive the Einstein–Bose statistics in a natural and almost "automatic" way. He suggested as before that at low temperatures there may be difficulties with degeneration or con-densation; as is well known today, the condensation of a gas into a liquid has indeed been connected with Einstein–Bose statistics.[56] Finally, Schrödinger remarked that the statistics are properly applied to energy levels and not to individual molecules. This method seemed so straight-forward that he referred to the Bose-statistical point of view as only a temporary expedient (*Durchgangstadium*), pending the application of "natural" statistics to the "proper" set of objects—surely a profound and prophetic remark.

Schrödinger did not continue to work on the subject of the statistics of elementary particles, but reviewing its development with the assistance of the new quantum mechanics, he produced a marvelously clear and concise account of the statistical theory of thermodynamics and some of its basic applications in his book, *Statistical Thermodynamics*, based on seminar lectures in 1944 at the Dublin Institute for Advanced Studies.[57] Here he offered a unified treatment capable of dealing with "every new problem that may arise" and, as he put it, "not a first introduction for newcomers... but rather a 'repetitorium.'" Schrödinger devoted much time to clarifying some of the knotty basic problems that were often slighted in standard books—such problems as that of the Nernst heat theorem and the $N!$ difficulty, the Bose condensation and degeneracy, the concealment of degenerate effects by Van der Waals forces, zero-point energy in crystals and the lack of particle-individuality in such cases, and the zero-point-energy problem for electromagnetic radiation (Planck's law).

[54] *Physik. Z.*, **27** (1926), 95–101.

[55] L. de Broglie, *Ann. de Physique*, **3** (1925), 22–128, also printed as *Thèses* (Paris: Masson, 1924). Also see Ch. III, sec. 3 below.

[56] *Statistical Thermodynamics*, Ch. VIII.

[57] *Ibid.*

In a popular and excellently written article on the individuality of elementary particles,[58] Schrödinger gave a particularly apt description of the "three statistics"—classical or Maxwell–Boltzmann, Einstein–Bose, and Fermi–Dirac. In brief, his example is as follows: Three boys, Tom, Dick, and Harry, representing three "states of motion," are eligible for two rewards, representing two "particles." There are three kinds of possible rewards, representing the three statistically-different types of entities. Classical particles are represented by two medals, one having a portrait of Newton and the other of Shakespeare. These rewards are completely distinguishable, and either may go to each boy, making nine possible distributions. Einstein–Bose particles are represented by two coins of equal value, and thus indistinguishable. There are three ways in which two boys get one coin each, and three in which one boy gets two coins, or six possible distributions. Fermi–Dirac particles, e.g., electrons, are represented by memberships on the football team. Not only are all memberships identical, but no one boy can hold two of them. Only three ways of distributing this type of reward are possible. The impossibility of two "particles" occupying one "state" is a particular case of the Pauli exclusion principle which is equivalent to the assumption of Fermi–Dirac statistics.

4. THE FOUNDATIONS OF THE SECOND LAW AND THE DIRECTION OF TIME

One of the most fundamental of the great problems of physics is that of the validity and meaning of the Second Law of Thermodynamics, the law that order tends to disorder, or that the total entropy in the universe always increases. It was one of the greatest contributions of Boltzmann[59] to show that this law follows from nothing more than the existence of atoms, their large numbers in any finite physical system, and a suitable statistical assumption. No special mechanism for individual processes is needed to account for the increase of entropy.

The major difficulty with the theory of the Second Law appears when one tries to derive its irreversible or unidirectional characteristic from the

[58] "What is an Elementary Particle?" *Endeavour*, 9 (1950), 109–116; reprinted in *STM*, pp. 193–223; German translation in E. Schrödinger, *Was ist ein Naturgesetz? Beiträge zum naturwissenschaftlichen Weltbild* (München/Wien: R. Oldenbourg, 1962), pp. 121–143; hereafter cited as *WN*.

[59] See E. Schrödinger, *Nature*, 153 (1944), 704–705.

theory of the motion of atoms and molecules, which for both Newtonian and quantum mechanics is reversible. By reversibility, we mean the following: Given any pair of states of two (or more) colliding molecules that can be connected in one order by a particular variety of collision, there will exist another variety of collision that connects them in the reverse order. If the velocities (for instance) in the two states are v_1', v_1'', ... and v_2', v_2'', ..., then there will be not only a collision changing the 1's to the 2's, but another equally likely one changing the 2's to the 1's. How then, can the *essentially* irreversible behavior described by the Second Law be derived from such reversible foundations? Boltzmann's answer to this difficulty was contained in his "*H* Theorem" which proceeds from the assumption that molecular collisions can be treated on a basis of "molecular chaos." The quantity H measures the uniformity or randomness of a set of particles, and Boltzmann furnished a proof that it will steadily increase, in the statistical sense, towards a limit. The Ehrenfests gave a clear and critical presentation of the logical foundations of this proof and other contributions of Boltzmann.[60] In spite of this careful critique, many later authors have been dissatisfied with the *H*-theorem and its modifications, and the basic questions of irreversibility and the approach to equilibrium are not yet closed.[61]

Many detailed studies of the approach to equilibrium have been made. One such was the "urn" experiment of Kohlrausch and Schrödinger[62] which had been proposed by the Ehrenfests in 1907.[63] In this experiment, one imagines two urns A and B containing a total of 100 numbered balls. A method of repetitively selecting numbers from 1 to 100 at random is available; at each selection the corresponding ball is considered to have been shifted from the urn it was in to the other. If all the balls were originally in urn A, what is the character of the approach toward 50–50 division as drawings proceed? The paper reports on 5,000 drawings and gives a comparison of the experimental results with a quite extensive probability theory treatment. The "stationary state," reached after 200 trials, showed good agreement with the expected distribution of the difference $N_B - N_A$, except that the frequency for the values zero and

---

[60] P. and T. Ehrenfest, *The Conceptual Foundations of the Statistical Approach in Mechanics*, trans. M. J. Moravcsik (Ithaca: Cornell University Press, 1959).

[61] See, for instance, H. Reichenbach, *The Direction of Time* (Berkeley: University of California Press, 1956).

[62] K. W. F. Kohlrausch and E. Schrödinger, *Physik. Z.*, **27** (1926), 306–313.

[63] *Physik. Z.*, **8** (1907), 311–314.

two were exceptionally high and the two signs of difference appeared distinctly asymmetrical. The approach to equilibrium followed the expected exponential law, as well as could be determined with the available data.

With respect to time reversal, Schrödinger carried out a simple and interesting calculation in connection with particle diffusion by asking an unusual type of question: If the location of a diffusing particle (e.g., in Brownian motion) is known at time t_0 and at time t_2, what is the probability of its having been at one particular place at t_1, where $t_0 < t_1 < t_2$?[64] This question involves a combination of prediction and retrospection, and illustrates symmetry with respect to t and $-t$. Only if the question is primarily predictive *or* retrospective, does there appear to be a difference between the two signs for the time.

Schrödinger's effort to restate the entropy-increase problem in a transparent way was made in 1933[65] and first published in 1950.[66] In contrast to Born's effort to use quantum uncertainties to solve the problem,[67] Schrödinger preferred to let the direction of time be determined by the entropy change. A brief and somewhat modified description of his argument is as follows:[68] If we consider a system with a large number of molecules over a long passage of the "mechanical" time variable t, there will occur fluctuations in a more or less regular way. Each fluctuation that might be noticed as such on a graph appears as a "motion" away from equilibrium followed by a roughly symmetrical motion back again. If we classify such fluctuations by their maximum "displacement," their distribution will be Gaussian, that is, exponential with a negative power which is proportional to the square of the displacement.[69] There will be many slight deviations and very few larger ones.

Now, suppose we happen to notice at one time a displacement from equilibrium which, however established, could be treated as part of a possible natural sequence. Any particular amount of deviation could be on the "moving away" or the "returning" part of a fluctuation

[64] *S. B. Preuss. Akad. Wiss.* (1931), 144–153.
[65] *S. B. Preuss. Akad. Wiss.* (1933), 165. (This is an abstract of the article in ref. 66.)
[66] *Proc. R. Irish Acad.*, 53A (1950), 189–195.
[67] *Natural Philosophy of Cause and Chance* (Oxford, 1949), pp. 70–73 and 120–121.
[68] The essence of this argument was given by the Ehrenfests; see ref. 60.
[69] See ref. 62.

whose maximum depth is greater than the initially observed amount, or it could be at the maximum depth. Because of the exponential distribution referred to, it is much more likely to be near the maximum of a shallow fluctuation than on the slope of a deeper one, and thus is likely to be followed by a return to the mean value.

Thus, with the passage of time in *either* direction, equilibrium will very nearly always be approached, and the experience of irreversibility follows directly from the reversible model. It is only necessary to say that the *actual physical direction* of time is that for which the entropy increases. Strictly, then, Schrödinger did not derive irreversibility, but by defining time in this way he did remove the possibility of logical contradiction in any such derivation.[70]

The concept of time's "arrow" as determined by the increase of entropy is an intriguing and puzzling one. Schrödinger subsequently referred to it in three places[71] and, in fact, related it to his belief in the indestructibility of mind.[72] However, this statistical concept of time does not seem very convincing. Among other things, it leads to the speculative and unlikely but conceivable consequence which Boltzmann had seen, namely, the possibility that time might "run the other way" in a distant part of the universe.

In fact, Schrödinger himself provided a different clue to the proper definition of the direction of time. In the first chapter of *Mind and Matter* he suggested that consciousness is in its very essence a matter of the experience of novelty—of new sensations and new manipulations. Anything that becomes completely habitual is lost to consciousness. But newness is directly related to the boundary-line between the unknown future and the remembered past. The consequence is, one can argue, that our experience of time is a measure of our very existence as conscious beings. We can relate the rational experiences of scientific activity to this basic existential fact of time, but can scarcely reverse the relation for purposes of a definition of time in any basic sense. An analysis of the

[70] For an excellent discussion of the difficulties with the concept of the direction of time and its possible reversal, as well as extensive references to the history of the idea of relating the direction of time to the increase in entropy, see M. Čapek, *Philosophical Impact of Contemporary Physics* (Princeton: D. Van Nostrand, 1961), Ch. XVII.

[71] *Nature*, **153** (1944), 704–705; "Der Geist der Naturwissenschaft," published in English as "The Spirit of Science" in *WIL*, pp. 245–250; *Mind and Matter* (Cambridge: Cambridge University Press, 1959). Hereafter cited as *MM*.

[72] *MM*, pp. 86–87.

problem of freedom and choice seems to indicate that the intentions and knowledge involved in the making of decisions also reflect our existence as time-experiencing beings.[73] (See Ch. V, pp. 144–146.)

Schrödinger did not actually contradict this view, for he maintained that what is required is a definition for the "*t*" in the equation.[74] In any given mathematical description of nature, does t or $-t$ correspond to the time of our basic experience? This is the question to be answered by the observed entropy change. Such a view allows our subjective experience of time to remain fundamental, but leaves the puzzle of what it could mean for time to run the other way in some distant place.

5. THE BASICALLY STATISTICAL NATURE OF PHYSICS

Franz Exner's textbook, written in 1917 and published two years later,[75] contains a concluding section on natural law, which Schrödinger summarized in his inaugural lecture at Zurich (1922)[76] and mentioned on numerous occasions as late as 1958.[77] Exner's study is clear, pedagogical, and somewhat repetitive. Not being in the form of a scholarly paper, it received little attention, even after the significance of its ideas had become evident through the development of quantum mechanics. It was not until 1929 that Schrödinger published his 1922 address; other physicists seem to have completely ignored Exner's work.[78]

Nevertheless, the importance of Exner's work for the development of Schrödinger's later thought is great. The main question for Exner is whether the laws of physics are exact and absolute, applying rigorously

---

[73] See E. Schrödinger, *Nature*, **138** (1936), 13–14.

[74] See ref. 66.

[75] *Vorlesungen über die physikalischen Grundlagen der Naturwissenschaften* (Vienna: Deuticke, 1919), Part IV, "Über Naturgesetze," Lectures 86–95. O. T. Benfey's translation of E. Cassirer's *Determinism and Indeterminism* (see ref. 78 below) mistakenly implies in footnote 8, p. 79, that Exner's work has been translated. Actually, it was Schrödinger's speech about Exner that was translated (see ref. 76 below).

[76] "Was ist ein Naturgesetz?" *Naturwissenschaften* **17** (1929), 9–11; reprinted in *WN*, pp. 9–17; trans. James Murphy, "What Is a Law of Nature?" *STM*, pp. 133–147.

[77] *Nuovo Cimento*, **9** (1958), 162–170. (Lecture delivered March 26, 1958, to the Austrian Physical Society and the Austrian Chemical-Physical Society.)

[78] E. Cassirer gave a careful and extensive account of Exner's work in *Determinism and Indeterminism in Modern Physics*, trans. O. T. Benfey (New Haven: Yale University Press, 1956), pp. 79–88.

to all cases, everywhere, for all time intervals. Admittedly, many laws involve simplifications, as in the kinetic theory of ideal non-interacting molecules that leads to the ideal gas law $PV = nRT$, or in the law of falling bodies that assumes no extraneous influences. But Exner was concerned whether "absolute" laws would exist if these simplifications and restrictions could be removed. He argued persuasively that such absoluteness comes from habits of thought, from deeply ingrained metaphysical presuppositions that have been taken as truths. However, when the method of verification of theories by experiment is applied, we readily see that we only test the laws within certain limits of space, time, and mass (quite aside from the problem of the errors of measurement). We do not know, for instance, if our ordinary physical laws hold for extremely small time intervals, and we only test them for macroscopic masses, i.e., for large numbers of atoms. Thus, our observations are basically statistical, and the laws of physics are statistical (*Durchschnittsgesetze*).

What, then, of the principle of causality? According to Exner, it has evolved out of mankind's age-long experience of regularity in nature coupled with a philosophical desire for absoluteness. There are, however, no logical or experimental grounds for extrapolating our experience of even approximate causality to the molecular realm. We can, of course, not deny the *possibility* of causality or determinism[79] on the molecular level, but a more homogeneous picture of the universe results if we assume both macrocosmos and microcosmos to obey laws of a basically statistical type than if we picture the former (as we must) as ultimately statistical, and the latter as strictly dynamical. In fact, the regularity we do observe appears to be "strict" or "exact" only in the limiting case of objects with infinitely large numbers of atoms.

In his Zurich speech, Schrödinger pointed out the circularity of using Newtonian mechanics for atomic systems, since this theory of mechanics only has meaning and validity in the realm of very large numbers of atoms. Even when we study individual atomic processes, we use apparatus composed of enormous numbers of molecules. Schrödinger, like Exner, objected to a dualism in nature in which large-scale physical events follow the laws of number and small-scale occurrences depend on

---

[79] A distinction between causality and determinism is not drawn in this discussion. For a careful account of these and related terms see M. Bunge, *Causality* (Cambridge, Mass.: Harvard University Press, 1958), Ch. I.

some mysterious "dark, eternally unintelligible imperative."[80] In fact, he even suggested (as Exner and Boltzmann had before him)[81] that gravitation may be a statistical phenomenon. Furthermore, energy and momentum may only be conserved on the average, and the intrinsic inconsistency in the laws of electrodynamics that seriously challenged the Bohr type of quantum theory[82] might also be overcome when "once we have discarded our rooted predilection for absolute causality."[83]

In the volume containing the translation of the Zurich speech, three later articles presented the argument that we are free to choose between a basically causal and a basically statistical atomic theory. In one, a paper originally read before the Congress of the Society for Philosophical Instruction in 1931,[84] Schrödinger gave an account of the growing conviction since 1900 among physicists that nature is not deterministic, a conviction grounded both in the history of the continued failure of determinism and in the successes of the indeterministic quantum theory. Nevertheless, he pointed out that no demonstration can be made of the impossibility of deterministic models.[85] In a 1935 paper on the law of chance, he suggested that we may follow Hume, if we wish, and treat the causal principle as a convenient habit of thought without objective grounds, or we may assume a rigid causality for atomic events.[86] The latter assumption is conservative, the former, revolutionary. Schrödinger believed that philosophical criticism clearly was becoming more impor-

---

[80] See ref. 76, *STM*, p. 145; *WN*, p. 15.

[81] Exner, *op. cit.*, p. 658, reports a conversation with Boltzmann on this matter.

[82] O. W. Richardson in *The Electron Theory of Matter* (2nd. ed.; Cambridge: Cambridge University Press, 1916), pp. 507–508, suggests that perhaps we cannot represent physical phenomena by any type of three-dimensional spatial geometry. See Ch. III, pp. 48–50 below, where there is a discussion of the famous effort of Bohr, Kramers, and Slater to construct a theory in which energy and momentum are only statistically conserved.

[83] Ref. 76, *STM*, p. 147; *WN*, p. 17.

[84] "Über Indeterminismus in der Physik" (Leipzig: J. A. Barth, 1932), lecture dedicated to F. Exner and delivered June 16, 1931; trans. J. Murphy, "Indeterminism in Physics," *STM*, pp. 52–80.

[85] David Bohm has developed this point in *Causality and Chance in Modern Physics* (Princeton: D. Van Nostrand, 1957; New York: Harper Torchbooks, 1961), Ch. IV. In fact, Bohm, de Broglie, Vigier, and others have produced a deterministic form of quantum theory which bases the presently known structure of matter on a lower level of a mechanistic type. See D. Bohm, R. Schiller, and J. Tiomno, *Nuovo Cimento*, 1 (1955), Supp. 1, 48–66.

[86] "The Law of Chance: The Problem of Causation in Modern Science," *STM*, pp. 39–51.

tant for physics; he saw that such criticism necessarily requires philosophers who have some intimate acquaintance with physics. Much the same idea is expressed in his third study, "Physical Science and the Temper of the Age."[87]

Another area of importance for causality is that of living processes, an area which Exner himself very carefully excluded from his discussion. Schrödinger, however, gave considerable attention to living processes and found, surprisingly, that the concepts of causality and determinism apply more generally and fundamentally to living organic systems than to the inorganic world. We shall take up his view in more detail in Chapter V, considering here only his remark on the so-called "regularities of nature" which have presumably led mankind into a belief in causality.

Schrödinger believed that we actually experience regularity in the form of many specific causal chains of events, in which certain relations stand out as necessary connections and other possible causal influences are unknown or overlooked. In general, these causal chains appear to us to be independent of each other. A causal view of the world around us extrapolates from these separate and distinct chains of events to an overall linking together of all occurrences. Schrödinger pointed out that we actually experience many chancelike intersections of these causal chains and that these random coincidences play a very large and most interesting part in the life around us.[88] (See Ch. V, pp. 123 and 131.) The transparent causal chains we make so much of in philosophical speculation actually function as a kind of "keyboard on which the often beautiful, often horrible, but ultimately always somehow meaningful harmony is being played."[89]

6. ATOMISM AND THE CONTINUUM

A particular characteristic of causal theories in classical physics is that of continuity and contiguity. Not only is determinism basically equivalent to the applicability of differential equations to the systems under consideration,[90] but it involves contiguous action. Causal theories generally

[87] *Ibid.*, pp. 106–132.

[88] "On the Peculiarity of the Scientific World View," *WIL*, pp. 201–202; *WN*, pp. 52–54.

[89] *WIL*, p. 202; *WN*, p. 54.

[90] H. Margenau, *The Nature of Physical Reality* (New York: McGraw-Hill, 1950) sec. 19.5.

have been expressed as field theories in which the action of a distant object on another is described in terms of a "field" radiated or generated by one object and propagated in space so that it can act at the position of the other object. Such theories require partial differential equations, using both space and time as independent variables. As Schrödinger described it: "What happens anywhere at any given moment depends only and unambiguously on what has been going on in the immediate neighborhood 'just a moment earlier.'"[91]

Before the advent of relativity theory, it was fairly easy to translate a field theory into an action-at-a-distance theory and vice versa. Contiguity was needed only as a convenience to thought. In fact, the notion that contiguity is fundamental because forces are basically pushes or pulls like those we know from touch and from rods and strings, etc., collapsed under the realization that atoms are undoubtedly nearly empty. The hard elastic-sphere picture of the atom which put the "push" into our picture of nature was lost. Action-at-a-distance came to seem more fundamental in the light of modern atomic theory.[92]

However, the concept of relativity with transmission of all effects at speeds equal to or less than the speed of light led to the notion of traveling fields carrying energy and momentum. Continuity itself would be lost if we had to conceive of momentum as emitted at one instant and absorbed at a later without "being somewhere" in between. This abrogation of continuity actually can be maintained in a logical, if cumbersome way, but few physicists have taken the possibility seriously.[93] The field concept for deterministic theories in physics seems to be here to stay, in spite of the seemingly fundamental character of action-at-a-distance.

The principle of continuity in space and time has had, as we shall see, both success and failure in quantum theory and played a considerable role in Schrödinger's own interests. In brief, the Schrödinger wave equation provides a continuous space-time description in terms of the wave functions of atomic systems, which nevertheless fails to describe

---

[91] *SH*, p. 29.

[92] The idea that the desire for contiguous action was due to the prejudice of our conditioned imaginations occurred to Boscovich, Kant, J. S. Mill, Comte, Wundt, Stallo, and Mach, among others. See M. Čapek, ref. 70, p. 92. Schrödinger gave a clear discussion of the usual transition in science from a discrete set of observations to a continuous theory in "Die Wandlung des physikalischen Weltbegriffs," *WN*, pp. 19–26.

[93] J. A. Wheeler and R. P. Feynman, *Rev. Mod. Phys.*, **21** (1949), 425–433, and **17** (1945), 157–181.

physical *events* in a causal way. Furthermore, the continuous properties of the wave equation themselves lead to quantum discreteness in energy, angular momentum, and other variables.

Before considering these questions, we shall note some of the difficulties involved in the very idea of the continuum, and review the Greek origins of atomism and the struggle over continuity. The study of these matters was another important stimulus to Schrödinger's scientific thought.

Anyone who has studied modern mathematics (e.g., the work of Dirichlet, Dedekind, Cantor) is familiar with the intricacy of the continuum. We become so accustomed in elementary calculus to the idea of a function $f(x)$ in which x can take on any value continuously (at least in a certain range of values) that it takes some training to appreciate the very real difficulties actually involved in this concept.

In physics, we approximate the ideal of continuity because we can only distinguish a finite number of different values of x, namely a set of values which are separated from each other by an amount just barely larger than our limits of measuring accuracy in a given circumstance; also, of course, we can only measure the numbers corresponding to the function $f(x)$ to a limited accuracy. But if we allow "every" value of x to be important, we run into such paradoxes as the one Schrödinger describes lucidly in *Science and Humanism*.[94] The number of values is so vast that we can take "nearly every" one away and have "as many" left as we had before!

In the example Schrödinger referred to, the middle third of the set of real numbers between 0 and 1 is removed, then the middle thirds of the remainders, the middle thirds of the next remainders, and so forth, each time leaving behind the upper end point of each group. After n removals, the fraction left is $(2/3)^n$, which gets smaller and smaller. Yet, by use of number notations based both on the base of 2 and on the base of 3, in place of our usual decimal notation based on 10, Schrödinger showed that the numbers remaining can be put into one-to-one correspondence with the original set, so that, in this sense, there are "just as many" left.

Schrödinger's book *Nature and the Greeks*[95] grew out of his interest in the origins of atomism. We shall consider the philosophical import of this work in detail in Chapter V, section 3, but Schrödinger's account of Greek ideas on atoms and continuity belong more properly in this chapter.

---

[94] Pages 29 ff.
[95] Pages 34–36; see ref. 32, Ch. I, p. 21.

Erwin Schrödinger

The Greeks of the Pythagorean school developed their ideas of geometry and numbers around the concept of the ratio of integers—for instance, by using the ratio of the numbers of dots on two sides of a figure made of a regular array of dots such as a triangle or square.[96] It was a profoundly disturbing event when it was proved that the diagonal of a square is not related to its side by a ratio of integers.[97] In fact, there is little doubt that this discovery led to the downfall of the Pythagorean order.[98] Euclidean geometry is, of course, able to handle such irrational ratios.

The famous paradoxes of Zeno also exemplify the puzzlement of the Greeks about continuous events. Achilles can not beat the tortoise, for first he must get half-way to the tortoise, then half of the remainder, then half of that, and so on for an infinite series. It was not conceivable to Zeno that an infinite series of events could add up to a finite total time—so the argument seemed to deny Achilles' evident ability to overtake the tortoise.

As Schrödinger pointed out, these and similar difficulties are closely related to the problem of explaining change in the physical world. How can water expand as it warms up? How can it evaporate into 1600 or 1700 times its liquid volume? Anaximenes (d. 526 B.C.), following Thales and Anaximander in assuming the existence of one basic type of material or element of which all things are made, accounted for the most obvious transformations of matter in terms of rarefaction and condensation.[99] The difficulties of the continuum and a deep practicing interest in geometry led Democritus (b. 460 B.C.) to account for rarefaction and condensation and, in fact, all physical occurrences by a theory of invisibly small atoms, perpetually moving in empty space.

Thus was born one of the great concepts of all science, not on grounds of evidence, but out of the intellectual passion for rationality.[100] Epicurus,

[96] *Ibid.*, pp. 34–36.

[97] If the side is 1 and the diagonal were p/q where p and q are integers with no common factor then we must have $(p/q)^2 = p^2/q^2 = 2$, or an irreducible fraction is equal to an integer, which is impossible.

[98] K. R. Popper, *Brit. Journ. for Phil. of Sci.*, **3** (1953), 124–156, reprinted in K. R. Popper, *Conjectures and Refutations: The Growth of Scientific Knowledge* (New York: Basic Books, 1962), pp. 66–96.

[99] *NG*, pp. 57–62.

[100] For a systematic account of the role of intellectual passions in the development of science, see M. Polanyi, *Personal Knowledge* (Chicago: University of Chicago Press, 1958; New York: Harper Torchbooks, 1964), especially Ch. 6.

whose interest was more religious than scientific, wrote an account of the atomic theory which was studied by Gassendi (b. 1592), who in turn revived the idea for modern science and made it possible for Dalton (b. 1766) to introduce an atomic explanation of the facts of chemistry. Ostwald and Mach rejected atomism as unnecessary;[101] it was Boltzmann and Maxwell who lifted atoms to the status of physical reality.[102] The theoretical explanation of Brownian motion by Einstein constituted the first of a long line of impressive results in atomic physics.[103]

It is not at all surprising that Schrödinger was interested in the history of atomism, but his main concern with Greek science stemmed from a deep interest in the problem of the philosophical and religious outlook of our times and in the struggles within physics itself to adjust to the quantum revolution. We shall return to these interests in the last chapters.

[101] *NG*, p. 74; M. Čapek, *op. cit.*, p. 100 and notes 13 and 14, p. 118.

[102] E. Schrödinger, "Unsere Vorstellung von der Materie," in *L'homme devant la science*, the Proceedings of the Rencontres Internationales de Genève, 1952 (Neuchâtel: éditions de Baconnière, 1952) and *WN*, pp. 102–120; trans. as "Our Conception of Matter," *WIL*, pp. 161–177.

[103] See *SH*, pp. 13–16.

Chapter III

The Development of Wave Mechanics

Schrödinger's invention of wave mechanics occurred at a time when the Bohr theory had passed its zenith and was creating more difficulties than successes in its further ramifications. Wave mechanics was an effort to resolve these difficulties by following the inspiration of de Broglie's concept of matter waves. The roots of the new mechanics went back to optical aspects of the Hamiltonian form of classical mechanics, and its further development involved union with the independently developed theory of matrix mechanics to form the inclusive theory now called quantum mechanics. An adequate account of Schrödinger's development of wave mechanics must include some of the history of the Bohr theory, the principal ideas of de Broglie, the beginnings of matrix mechanics, and Hamiltonian "optics."

1. THE BOHR THEORY

In 1913, shortly after his arrival at the laboratory in Manchester where Rutherford and his group were working out the newly discovered theory of the nuclear atom,[1] Niels Bohr developed his theory of the hydrogen atom and its spectrum.[2] His most important new concept was that classical mechanics could be expected to apply to mean values only and hence could be used for stationary states but not for periods of transition.

---

[1] A brief and illuminating historical account of the events in Manchester at this time is given by C. G. Darwin, "The Discovery of Atomic Number," in *Niels Bohr and the Development of Physics,* ed. W. Pauli (New York: McGraw-Hill, and London: Pergamon, 1955), pp. 1–11.

[2] *Phil. Mag.*, **26** (1913), 1–25, 476–502, 857–877. The first part of this paper contains the basic advance; a summary is given at the end of the third part. Most of parts II and III deal with efforts which later did not prove useful for applying the theory to many-particle systems.

The stability of atoms and the constancy of spectral frequencies were accounted for by assuming radiation to occur only during transitions between stationary states, thus implying that the classical electrodynamics of radiation by accelerated (revolving) charges did not hold. The Planck formula $\Delta E = h\nu$, relating energy and frequency of radiation, was applied to transitions, but classical physics, or even the possibility of a causal picture, was abandoned for the description of these transitions. Partly because of this very lack of description, the transitions were called "jumps." The question whether transitions are continuous or discontinuous will be discussed at some length below and in the next chapter.

The introduction of the Planck constant h made it possible to form another constant, of the dimensions of a length, of the correct magnitude to give the size of the atom, using the already available values of the mass and charge of the electron. (The velocity of light, c, was not expected to enter because the energies are nonrelativistic; moreover, magnetic forces were not assumed to be important.) This value, the so-called Bohr radius $a_0 = h^2/4\pi^2me^2 = 0.528 \times 10^{-8}$ cm, is still the basic unit of length for theories of atomic structure. Furthermore, the value of the Rydberg constant, relating the frequencies of the spectral lines of hydrogen and the enumeration integers used in Balmer's formula, was predicted almost exactly by Bohr's theory. Later, when the motion of the nucleus was taken into account, experiment and theory came into precise agreement. Actually, Arthur Haas had already discovered the formula for the atomic radius by using the Thomson model of the hydrogen atom, assuming that the limit of the Balmer series gave the frequency of steady rotation of the electron and taking the radius of the orbit equal to the radius of the sphere of positive charge.[3]

The rule determining which orbits were the stable ones was first described by Bohr in terms of energy and rotational frequency and then shown to be most simply stated in terms of angular momentum: the angular momentum p_ϕ of an electron in a stationary state is an integral multiple of $h/2\pi$. The rule was, of course, chosen to give results in agreement with the Balmer formula.[4] K. F. Herzfeld also

[3] A. E. Haas, *S. B. Akad. Wiss. Wien*, Abt. 2a, **119** (1910), 119–144.

[4] J. W. Nicholson was the first to relate Planck's constant and angular momentum. See *Monthly Notices Roy. Astron. Soc.*, **72** (1912), 677. The quantization of angular momentum had been suggested by W. Nernst, *Zeits. f. Elektrochem.*, **17** (1911), 265–275. Following work of N. Bjerrum, P. Ehrenfest obtained the correct rule simultaneously with, but independent of, Bohr, *Verh. d. deutsch. Phys. Ges.*, **15** (1913), 451–457.

constructed a Thomson type of model which could emit the Balmer series.[5]

Bohr chiefly considered circular orbits and assumed that the quantum condition applied only to them. Efforts to extend the rule to elliptical orbits and to rotating molecules, as well as to other cases, led to a generalization found independently and almost simultaneously by W. Wilson,[6] A. Sommerfeld,[7] and J. Ishiwara,[8] i.e., that for generalized coordinates, when each p_k depends only on its q_k, the integral $\oint p_k \, dq_k$ taken over a cycle of periodicity is an integral multiple of h:

$$\oint p_k \, dq_k = nh. \tag{1}$$

In the dozen years which followed Bohr's first paper, his theory was considerably developed. It proved an excellent first approximation for the exploration of atomic and molecular spectra and several types of atomic collision experiments.[9] Such items as the fine structure in the spectra of hydrogen, ionized helium and the alkali elements, the Zeeman effect, the Stark effect, multiplets (after Goudsmit and Uhlenbeck introduced the concept of spin[10]), rotational-vibrational molecular spectra, the Raman effect, resonance radiation, dispersion, and molecular dissociation, all found explanations in what generally became known as the Bohr–Sommerfeld theory.[11]

[5] *S. B. Akad. Wiss. Wien*, Abt. 2a, **121** (1912), 593–601.

[6] *Phil. Mag.*, **29** (1915), 795–802. In a later note, *Phil. Mag.*, **31** (1916), 156–162, this author compares his results with the similar but not equivalent proposal of J. Ishiwara (ref. 8 below).

[7] *Ann. der. Physik*, **51** (1916), 1–94, esp. p. 9. Sommerfeld acknowledges the priority of Wilson. (He refers to him as "A. Wilson" and cites Wilson's 1916 article as published in "November, 1915.")

[8] *Math. Phys. Soc. Tokyo*, **8** (1915), 106–116, 173–186, and 318–327.

[9] Ruark and Urey, *Atoms, Molecules, and Quanta* (New York: McGraw-Hill, 1930) give an excellent and detailed account of the successes and limitations of the Bohr–Sommerfeld theory. Other good accounts are found in A. Sommerfeld, *Atomic Structure and Spectral Lines*, trans. H. L. Brose (3rd ed.; New York: E. P. Dutton, 1923); E. N. da C. Andrade, *Structure of the Atom* (3rd ed.; New York: Harcourt Brace, 1927); F. Reiche, *The Quantum Theory*, trans. H. S. Hatfield and H. L. Brose (2nd ed.; New York: E. P. Dutton, 1930); G. Birtwistle, *The Quantum Theory of the Atom* (Cambridge: Cambridge University Press, 1926); and F. K. Richtmyer, *Introduction to Modern Physics* (1st ed.; New York: McGraw-Hill, 1928). Bohr's own summary is given in *Naturwissenschaften*, **14** (1926), 1–10, a report of a speech Aug. 30, 1925, to the Scandinavian Mathematics Congress.

[10] S. A. Goudsmit and G. E. Uhlenbeck, *Nature*, **117** (1926), 264–265, and *Naturwissenschaften*, **13** (1925), 953–954.

[11] See ref. 9.

This theory, however, had several serious difficulties. At several points in the theory half-odd-integers (1/2, 3/2, etc.) had to be inserted for the integer n in the rule (1). Efforts to construct a theory of a stable system of more than two particles, e.g., the helium atom with a nucleus and two electrons, failed miserably. The intensities of spectral lines were calculated approximately by use of the correspondence principle, but the deliberate renunciation of any description of the transition process prevented a more satisfactory derivation.

Chaturvedi's estimate of the transition time for an electron jump[12] illustrated the serious difficulties involved in retaining as much of ordinary mechanics as was included in the Bohr theory. Any method of estimating gives the number of wave lengths in an emitted wave train as about one, in contrast to the estimate of 10^8 or so provided by Michelson's work on coherence lengths.[13]

2. MATRIX MECHANICS

Although the matrix and wave forms of quantum mechanics[14] were proven to be logically equivalent within two months of the discovery of the latter, a separate discussion of the former is appropriate here. Werner Heisenberg was impressed by the success of Ladenburg and Kramers in forming a theory of optical dispersion[15] that referred to the observable mechanical details of the stationary states themselves. He tried formulating quantum theory by use of analogies to classical *problems* (i.e., equations of motion), rather than to the classical *solutions* of these problems. In his first paper[16] he dealt with an anharmonic oscillator equation, representing coordinates q in terms of coefficients q_{nm} in Fourier series expansions involving all the frequencies that could be radiated or absorbed, $\nu_{nm} = (E_n - E_m)/h$. Squares and products of coordinates were

[12] R. K. Chaturvedi, *Z. Physik.* **33** (1925), 660–663.

[13] A. A. Michelson, *Phil. Mag.*, **31** (1891), 338–346, and **34** (1892), 280–299. See also O. Lummer and E. Gehrcke, *Verh. duetsch. Phys. Ges.*, **4** (1902), 337–346.

[14] The term "quantum mechanics" was first used in the literature of theoretical physics by M. Born, *Z. Physik*, **26** (1924), 279–395. See also E. T. Whittaker, *A History of the Theories of Aether and Electricity* (New York: Thomas Nelson, 1953), II, *The Modern Theories, 1900–1926*, p. 204.

[15] R. Ladenburg, *Z. Physik*, **4** (1921), 451–468. For a full account with other references, see Whittaker, *op. cit.*, II, pp. 200–205; also H. A. Kramers, *Nature*, **113** (1924), 673–674.

[16] W. Heisenberg, *Z. Physik*, **33** (1925), 879–893; this paper was received by the editor on July 29, 1925.

represented by series in which the coefficients were, for instance, $\sum_r x_{nr} y_{rm}$. An analogous equation to the quantum condition (1) was found by following Kramers' dispersion theory, but only in a form suitable for a few special cases. The method yielded correct values of frequencies and transition probabilities.

Shortly thereafter, Max Born (for whom Heisenberg was then serving as assistant) saw that Heisenberg's mathematical rules were the same as those applying to matrices, so that position and momentum were to be matrices **q**, **p** (of infinite order, in general) rather than ordinary numbers, and so obeyed a noncommutative algebra. Born and his other assistant, Pascual Jordan, deduced that the combination **pq** − **qp** must equal $h/2\pi i$ times the unit matrix,[17] giving the so-called commutation rule

$$\mathbf{pq} - \mathbf{qp} = (h/2\pi i)\mathbf{1} \tag{2}$$

which takes the place of the quantization rule (1) of the older quantum theory. Born and Jordan wrote the matrix analogs of the Hamiltonian equations of motion for a harmonic oscillator and found explicit expressions for the **q** and **p** matrices. In particular, the off-diagonal matrix elements contained information on the frequencies and intensities of spectral lines (transition rates), and the diagonal elements were related to the stationary states.

Meanwhile at Cambridge, Dirac was developing Heisenberg's idea by treating quantum-mechanical variables as new sorts of numbers, without specifying them as matrices that obeyed a noncommutative algebra.[18] Dirac found that the commutator **xy** − **yx** of any two variables was a direct analog of $ih/2\pi$ times the corresponding Poisson bracket in classical physics, $\sum_k [(\partial x/\partial q_k)(\partial y/\partial p_k) - (\partial x/\partial p_k)(\partial y/\partial q_k)]$. The quantum rule(2) then followed; in a later paper[19] Dirac referred to the independence of his discovery of eq. (2) from the work of Born and Jordan.

In the fall of 1925 Max Born spent some time at the Massachusetts Institute of Technology and developed with N. Wiener[20] the concept of using operators for the variables that were matrices for Born and Jordan and q-numbers for Dirac. Their concept had the generality needed to allow Schrödinger's wave mechanics and the Heisenberg–Born–Jordan

[17] M. Born and P. Jordan, *Z. Physik*, **34** (1925), 858–88; received Sept. 27, 1925.

[18] P. A. M. Dirac, *Proc. Roy. Soc.*, **109**A (1925), 642–653.

[19] *Proc. Roy. Soc.*, **110**A (1926), 561–579.

[20] M. Born and N. Wiener, *Z. Physik*, **36** (1926), 174–187; *Journ. Math. Phys.* (Mass. Inst. Tech.), **5** (1926), 84–98.

matrix mechanics to be subsumed under one very general scheme.[21] A paper by Born, Heisenberg, and Jordan[22] laid the general groundwork for matrix mechanics and led to a large number of further papers during the next few months, applying the new method in many ways. We shall not even try to detail this activity.[23]

3. DE BROGLIE'S THEORY

The papers of Louis de Broglie led Schrödinger to the invention of wave mechanics. De Broglie first published a series of six short papers in the *Comptes Rendues* of the Paris Academy,[24] then an article in the *Philosophical Magazine*,[25] and finally a beautifully written thesis.[26] Without giving a detailed account of his ideas, we shall indicate his chief contributions and some of their limitations.

De Broglie took as a starting point the validity of both the special theory of relativity and the Planck energy-frequency relation $E = h\nu$. Thus a vibration of frequency $\nu_0 = m_0 c^2/h$ is to be associated with the energy of a free particle at rest. The frequency as calculated in a different inertial frame, in which the particle has a constant velocity $v = \beta c$, has two contradictory values, i.e., the increased value $\nu_0(1 - \beta^2)^{-1/2}$ calculated from the increased mass, and the reduced value $\nu_0(1 - \beta^2)^{+1/2}$ calculated from the Lorentz dilation of time. De Broglie resolved this contradiction by associating the lower value with a vibration in (or at) the moving object and the increased value with a vibration in a wave moving with a speed

$$u = c/\beta = v/\beta^2. \tag{3}$$

This wave, called by de Broglie an "*onde de phase*," keeps in phase with the vibration in the moving object. Actually, it is not necessary to assume

[21] See P. A. M. Dirac, *The Principles of Quantum Mechanics* (1st ed.; Oxford: Clarendon Press, 1930); J. von Neumann, *Mathematische Grundlagen der Quantemechanik* (Berlin: J. Springer, 1932), trans. R. T. Beyer, *Mathematical Foundations of Quantum Mechanics* (Princeton: Princeton University Press, 1955).

[22] *Z. Physik*, **35** (1926), 557–615.

[23] For an account written in 1926, see L. Brillouin, "The New Atomic Mechanics" in *Wave Mechanics*, by L. de Broglie and L. Brillouin (London: Blackie and Son, 1928), pp. 19–53.

[24] *Comptes Rendues Acad. Sci.* (Paris), **177** (1923), 507–510, 548–550, 630–632.

[25] **47** (1924), 446–458.

[26] *Ann. de Physique*, **3** (1925), 22–128; also printed as *Thèses* (Paris: Masson, 1924).

two separate vibrations, but only to assume that the calculation of frequency from the time dilation gives the frequency to be observed at a point moving with speed $v = \beta c$ and that the frequency calculated from the energy-mass-speed relation is that observed at a fixed point in the observer's frame of reference as the wave goes by. If the phase of the wave is $\phi = 2\pi\nu(t - \beta x/c) = 2\pi\nu_0(t - \beta x/c)(1 - \beta^2)^{-1/2}$, and we observe the phase at points given by $x = \beta ct$, we have a time variation $\phi = 2\pi\nu_0 t(1 - \beta^2)^{1/2}$. The use of a phase speed greater than light causes no difficulty because the usual group velocity calculation yields a group velocity

$$v_g = d\nu/d(\nu/u) = \beta c = v. \qquad (4)$$

Thus out of the effort to join the well-established relativistic mechanics for a particle with the widely successful Planck–Einstein formula for vibratory phenomena came the idea not only of a vibration, but a wave, associated with a material particle. It immediately followed that the Bohr–Sommerfeld–Einstein quantization condition (1) was simply the assertion that whole numbers of wave lengths are to be found in any cyclic steady-state process.

Mechanics and optics appeared to be intertwined. De Broglie suggested that the wave not only travels with the particle, but that the object's motion is governed in some measure by wave dynamics. It was known that wave optics followed Fermat's principle of least time and led to the ordinary ray-optical behavior in regions where diffraction and interference were negligible. Perhaps Newtonian particle mechanics is similarly a ray-optical limit of a wave type of motion, and the basic dynamical principle is that particle paths are normals to wave fronts. More elegantly, the assertion is that the Fermat principle of least time and the Maupertius principle of least action are identical.

The Maupertius principle of least action may be obtained from Hamilton's principle which states that if we consider only variations for constant energy, the integral $\int_{t_1}^{t_2} \sum_k p_k \, dq_k$ taken between fixed times t_1 and t_2 has an extreme value. The Fermat principle asserts the extremal character for an integral along a wave normal of the phase integral $\int d\phi$. The equivalence between them implies (in a space-time formulation) that the phase expression $d\phi = \sum_k O_k \, dx^k$ is proportional to the energy-momentum expression $\sum_k p_k \, dx^k$; the vectors O_k and p_k must themselves be proportional. Since the time components are assumed to be related by

$$O_4 \, dx^4 = -2\pi\nu \, dt = -2\pi E \, dt/h = -(2\pi/h)(E/c)c \, dt \qquad (5)$$

44

we must have for the space components

$$O_i \, dx^i = 2\pi k_i \, dx^i = (2\pi/h)p_i \, dx^i. \tag{6}$$

In other words, the components of the wave vector k_i are equal to p_i/h and the wave length is given by

$$1/\lambda^2 = k_1{}^2 + k_2{}^2 + k_3{}^2 = (p_1{}^2 + p_2{}^2 + p_3{}^2)/h^2 = p^2/h^2 \tag{7}$$

or

$$\lambda = h/p \tag{8}$$

which is de Broglie's famous relation, verified in 1927 experimentally by Davisson and Germer[27] and by G. P. Thomson[28] after the study by Elsasser of certain earlier evidence.[29] De Broglie was also able to provide a preliminary justification of Planck's factor h^3 used to measure volume elements in phase space for statistical physics, a factor whose use was completely justified later in quantum statistical mechanics.

De Broglie attempted to create a theory of interference that would unite the wave and particle aspects of light. He assumed that his waves did not themselves carry energy (thus the existence of phase speeds greater than c was not uncomfortable), but that they somehow guided the energy which was in corpuscular form. To explain how a wave could spread out, a portion of it pass through each of two slits, and a regular pattern of arrival of quanta at the screen be governed by the resulting interference pattern of the waves, he suggested that stimulated emission in a group of atoms could result in a coherent wave carrying several quanta. The photons would arrive uniformly on the screen, but their probabilities of being absorbed would be governed by the wave amplitude.

In other words, de Broglie introduced a statistical hypothesis in order to unite the two aspects of matter and light. However, his form of the hypothesis, like that proposed independently and at about the same time by Bohr, Kramers, and Slater (see sec. 4 below), was doomed to contradiction by experiment. In fact, experimental results on interference

---

[27] C. J. Davisson and L. H. Germer, *Nature*, **119** (1927), 558–560; *Phys. Rev.*, **30** (1927), 705–740.

[28] G. P. Thomson and A. Reid, *Nature*, **119** (1927), 890–891; *Proc. Roy. Soc.*, **117**A (1928), 600–609.

[29] W. Elsasser, *Naturwissenschaften*, **13** (1925), 7–11. See also the discussion in Whittaker, *op. cit.*, II, pp. 217–219.

patterns produced in very weak light[30] seem quite incompatible with de Broglie's hypothesis, in spite of his own statement that his explanation holds, "however weak be the intensity of the incident light."[31]

The chief element that de Broglie was unable to provide in his theory was an actual wave equation to describe the propagation of his proposed matter waves, and it was, of course, exactly this equation that Schrödinger discovered. However, it should be pointed out that de Broglie dealt primarily with progressive waves in the relativistic region of energies. Schrödinger's opportunity to make his discovery came about partly because he primarily paid attention to *standing* waves. We shall also see that de Broglie's waves, in three-space even for many particles, were more intuitively "physical" than the quantitatively more successful but highly abstract waves in the space of quantum mechanics, whose dimensionality is three times the number of particles in the system.

4. EARLY WORK OF SCHRÖDINGER

We have already noted Schrödinger's work of a statistical nature on specific heats and gas theory, work that either uses the old Bohr theory or bears directly on wave mechanical ideas (Ch. II, above). A number of other papers should also be mentioned as precursors to the discovery of wave mechanics.

Schrödinger made several direct contributions to the Bohr-Sommerfeld theory. The most important of these was the concept of the penetration of the orbit of an outer electron into the next inner, filled shell.[32] A rough model involving a change from one ellipse to another as the electron gets into the closed shell was used to account for the nonintegral quantum numbers in the Balmer-like formulas for alkali spectra. Schrödinger referred to this discovery of "dipping tracks" (*Tauchbahnen*) in the autobiography he prepared for the Nobel prize ceremonies[33] as "a small but positive detail of success." His later paper on the electric polarizability of the inner shells (kernel or *Rumpf*) of alkali atoms[34] represented a

---

[30] A. J. Dempster and H. F. Batho, *Physical Rev.* **30** (1927), 644–648. See also Whittaker, *op. cit.*, II, p. 94.

[31] *Comptes Rendues Acad. Sci.* (Paris), **177** (1923), 548–550.

[32] *Z. Physik*, **4** (1921), 347–354.

[33] *Les Prix Nobel en 1933*, M. C. G. Santesson, ed. (Stockholm: Imprimerie Royale, P. A. Norstedt en Söner, 1935), pp. 86–88. Schrödinger mistakenly dates the paper cited in ref. 32 as "1920."

[34] *Ann. Physik.*, **77** (1925), 43–70.

further "minor success" but, like the earlier one, had no direct bearing on wave mechanics.

In 1922, Schrödinger pointed out a curious application of Weyl's space-time theory to the older quantum theory.[35] If the electron has a characteristic size or length, this length may alter with motion in accordance with the affine connection that relates the metric between one point and another. The amount of alteration turns out to be proportional to the quantity $\sum_k p_k \, dq_k$. If we use the quantum condition (1), we find that the characteristic length is multiplied, after one period, by a factor $\exp(nh/\gamma)$, where γ is a constant to be determined. Schrödinger suggested that it might be $h/2\pi i$, thus hinting at a sort of "phase factor" considerably before the wave idea was applied to electrons.

His subsequent work on thermal equilibrium between light and sound waves was an effort to use both energy and momentum considerations for the interaction between waves of different frequencies.[36] The results were not particularly significant, since the interactions were experimentally unobservable. (Similar interactions between X-rays and crystal vibrations are, of course, important.) The treatment was statistical and is mentioned here only because of its focus on waves.

A more interesting set of considerations before 1926 concerned the problem of "needle radiation." J. J. Thomson had observed in 1903 that the ionization of hydrogen gas by X-rays requires for its explanation either a "graininess" in the radiation or the existence of a very small proportion of hydrogen molecules that are vastly more ionizable than the rest.[37] The following year he suggested that each quantum of energy radiated is sent out in a narrow "needle" or cone of small angular aperture.[38] Einstein showed that the Planck radiation law and the Bohr rule for the emission of radiation are only consistent if this concept is used.[39] In fact, conservation of momentum and energy in atomic processes requires a concentration of momentum as well as energy in the radiation (as shown later in the Compton effect), and any spreading out, even over a small angle, would lead to inconsistency.

Schrödinger became interested in whether, by demonstrating a wide

[35] *Z. Physik*, **12** (1922), 13–23.

[36] *Physik. Z.*, **25** (1924), 89–94.

[37] *The Conduction of Electricity Through Gases* (London: Cambridge University Press, 1903), p. 258.

[38] *Electricity and Matter*, Silliman Lectures (New Haven: Yale University Press, 1911), pp. 63–65.

[39] *Physik. Z.*, **18** (1917), 121–128.

angle of emission of a coherent beam, one could find interference phenomena that definitely contradicted this result. He carried out an experiment [*sic*!] with an optical bench[40] and demonstrated interference from two beams that left a single source 6° to 10° apart; with microscopes he was able to get up to 30° divergence. His sources were extremely thin glowing metal filaments, and his interference observations led to reasonable measurements of their diameters. However, he concluded that all he had demonstrated was that the Huygens–Kirchhoff principle can be used for light waves after emission, i.e., even needle-like emission would yield wide-angled virtual sources surrounding the emitter under conditions in which diffraction theory is applicable.

Be that as it may, the discovery of enormously wide coherent beams, e.g., those of more than 2 meters in width detected by Michelson in his stellar-interferometric measurement of the diameter of Betelgeuse,[41] made it very difficult to accept the needle-radiation hypothesis. Brillouin[42] nevertheless showed that quite general considerations concerning the equilibrium between black body radiation and atomic absorbers, whether or not the Bohr hypothesis was used, required a needlelike character of at least the fluctuating component of the radiation.

In another early paper, Schrödinger dealt with the recoil-stimulated Doppler shift occurring on emission of radiation by an atom.[43] This paper used the concepts of emission in "jumps" and of "needle-radiation," and introduced a suitable mean of the velocities before and after the transitions. Dirac simplified the result and provided a four-vector representation of it.[44]

The next step in the study of the structure of radiation that concerned Schrödinger was the famous attempt by Bohr, Kramers, and Slater to resolve the duality between spreading waves and localized transfers of energy and momentum.[45] They assumed that waves were constantly

---

[40] *Ann. Physik*, **61** (1919), 69–86. Reference is made to this work by W. Gerlach and A. Landé, *Z. Physik*, **36** (1926), 169–173.

[41] A. A. Michelson, *Astrophys. J.*, **51** (1920), 257–262; A. A. Michelson and F. G. Pease, *Astrophys. J.*, **53** (1921), 249–259.

[42] L. Brillouin, *J. Phys. Radium*, **2** (1921), 142–155.

[43] *Physik. Z.*, **23** (1922), 301–303.

[44] P. A. M. Dirac, *Proc. Camb. Phil. Soc.*, **22** (1924), 432–433.

[45] N. Bohr, H. A. Kramers, and J. C. Slater, *Phil. Mag.*, **47** (1924), 785–802, and *Z. Physik*, **24** (1924), 69–87. J. C. Slater, in *Nature*, **113** (1924), 307–308, introduced the assumption of the virtual radiation field by means of which atoms were continually in communication.

being emitted by an atom in a steady excited state and constantly influencing all other accessible atoms without transmitting energy. Very much as de Broglie had proposed, the wave was assumed to govern the probability of a transfer of energy.

The emission or absorption of the wave was assumed to cease at the moment of actual transition; in fact, the waves emitted or absorbed involved a superposition of all possible transition frequencies. Thus an energy change for a given atom would be statistically determined by the wave amplitude at the atom and not by the occurrence or absence of any transitions at other atoms. Energy, in other words, was assumed not to be conserved in individual atomic occurrences, but only on the average, i.e., statistically. The same had to be true of momentum. While radiation may have been emitted spherically from an atom, the momentum $h\nu/c$ associated with a quantum transition had to be emitted in a random but specific direction, like Thomson's needle radiation. The length of wave trains, as shown by Michelson's interferometric studies of coherence length (see pp. 41, 49) and also by the measurements of W. Wien on the life-time of excited states,[46] was thus explained as representing the time of emission of the virtual radiation and not the time of the energetic transition. Since these lifetimes ($\sim 10^{-8}$ sec) are often of the same order of magnitude as the time between collisions in a highly excited gas, this result was satisfactory.

Bohr, Kramers, and Slater assumed that energy would be conserved in interatomic collisions, but of course the Compton effect was not considered to be a collision between a "photon" and an atom. Rather, this effect involved the *continuous* absorption and reradiation of waves by the electron, with the acquisition of momentum and energy by the electron by a chance process.

The proposal that atomic physics is fundamentally statistical quite naturally appealed to Schrödinger, particularly the idea that energy as well as entropy is statistical. He promptly set about calculating some of the consequences.[47] Demonstrating his flair as a teacher, he offered a clear exposition of the main points of the BKS article, and then discussed the statistical fluctuations their model entails. This model requires that although the energy emitted by an atom in a transition from a higher state to a lower is a fixed amount, it occurs at random times, whereas the

[46] *Ann. Physik.*, **60** (1919), 597–637. For later references see H. Kerschbaum, *Ann. Physik.*, **83** (1927), 287–295.
[47] *Naturwissenschaften*, **12** (1924), 720–724.

rate of energy transfer in the waves must be taken as continuous, since its absorption by other atoms does not depend on transitions in the emitter.

Thus there will be considerable fluctuation in the amount of energy in an atom of a gas at thermal equilibrium, with mean-square deviation equal to the mean value (the same result as for time distributions in radioactive decay). If analyzed in terms of a large number of atoms at a temperature high enough for a given upper level to share in the equipartition of energy, the fluctuations for a time equal to the mean life of an excited state are approximately the same as would be calculated using the classical heat-bath arguments of thermodynamics. Further consideration showed that the larger fluctuations for longer times would not be readily observable. The relation to a heat-bath, or in general to the rest of the universe, is what brings stability to such a basically statistical nature of things. Schrödinger suggested in conclusion that the unity of nature is essential in the overcoming of chaos.

The hope that the method of Bohr, Kramers, and Slater would offer a way out of the dualistic difficulties was soon shattered. Bothe and Geiger[48] performed a coincidence experiment with the Compton effect to see if the ejected electron and the scattered photon could be caught simultaneously at the angles predicted by the use of the conservation laws. They found that such coincidences occurred at a frequency quite compatible with the assumption of conservation of energy and momentum in individual events, and too frequent by many orders of magnitude if the Bohr–Kramers–Slater assumptions were right.[49]

When Schrödinger turned to the wave concept later, he utilized a very different idea, that of *standing electron* waves in the atom rather than of *steadily radiated electromagnetic* waves from atoms, and he abandoned the statistical approach to the point that he was later to express misgivings about the statistical interpretations that Born gave to his own wave theory. We shall return to these matters later.

5. THE PAPERS ON WAVE MECHANICS

Summing up Schrödinger's contribution to quantum mechanics in an obituary notice,[50] Dirac noted that Schrödinger's first efforts took into

[48] W. Bothe and H. Geiger, *Z. Physik*, **32** (1925), 639–663.

[49] Bohr published a further article on the new theory after the work of Bothe and Geiger had come out, with a note added in proof announcing that the theory could not be correct: *Z. Physik*, **34** (1925), 142–157.

[50] *Nature*, **189** (1961), 355–356.

account relativistic mechanics for the motion of the electron. However, the results were not in agreement with observation—we know now that the failure was due to the omission of spin effects and not to any incorrectness of method—and Schrödinger, disappointed, dropped the work. Only later did he take up the nonrelativistic approximation and achieve success.

In the first of his famous papers on wave mechanics,[51] he stated that he had originally planned to introduce quantization by the "intuitive" method of inventing a function ψ which is to be associated in de Broglie's way with a vibration process in the atom. One then would look for an equation for ψ which would have a solution only for certain "characteristic" or "proper" values ("eigenvalues" or *eigenwerte*) of the energy.

However, he presented his method in this paper in a relatively abstract, "neutral" mathematical form, a form which he promptly abandoned as "external" in a second paper (see below, p. 52). Starting with the Hamilton–Jacobi (H–J) equation[52] in the form

$$H\left(q_1, \ldots, q_{3n}, \frac{\partial S}{\partial q_1}, \ldots, \frac{\partial S}{\partial q_{3n}}\right) = E \tag{9}$$

he made a change of dependent variable by the equation

$$S = K \log \psi \tag{10}$$

for which K is a constant of the dimensions of action (erg-sec). The new function ψ will be a product of functions of each q_k and all the $3n$ arbitrary constants P_k if S is a sum:

$$S = S_1(q_1; P_1, \ldots, P_{3n}) + S_2(q_2; P_1, \ldots, P_{3n}) + \cdots \\ + S_{3n}(q_{3n}; P_1, \ldots, P_{3n}). \tag{11}$$

Schrödinger then reduced the H–J equation to the form of a quadratic expression set equal to zero. The "external" approach consists in the bold step of abandoning the equality and instead setting equal to zero the variation of the volume integral of the quadratic form. The Eulerian

---

[51] *Ann. Physik*, **79** (1926), 361–376; received by the editor Jan. 27, 1926; trans. J. F. Shearer and W. M. Deans in *Collected Papers on Wave Mechanics* (London: Blackie and Son, 1928), pp. 1–12, cited hereafter as *WM*; Schrödinger, *Abhandlungen zur Wellenmechanik* (2nd ed.; Leipzig: J. A. Barth, 1928), pp. 1–16, cited hereafter as *AW*.

[52] For background in the principal ideas of Hamiltonian mechanics, see Herbert Goldstein, *Classical Mechanics* (Reading, Mass.: Addison-Wesley, 1950) Chs. 7 and 9, or any other standard text.

equation of this variational principle is just the ordinary Schrödinger equation:

$$\nabla^2\psi + \frac{2m}{K^2}(E - V)\psi = 0 \qquad (12)$$

subject also to the condition that ψ vanish suitably at infinity.

Choosing V to be the potential energy for a particle of charge $-e$ at a distance r from a fixed particle of charge $+e$, Schrödinger then proceeded to derive discrete negative energy and continuous positive energy eigenvalues for the single hydrogen atom. The solution of the eigenvalue problem was worked out in detail, using spherical harmonics and treating the radial equation by means of a Laplace transform, following methods of Poincaré and Horn.[53] The value of K needed to fit the Rydberg constant was exactly $h/2\pi$. Schrödinger assumed that the frequency of the vibration is proportional to E with a suitable large constant, possibly m_0c^2, added.[54]

Schrödinger suggested that several different vibrations might occur simultaneously, so that the difference frequencies of the Bohr condition correspond to beats between different proper vibrations. He believed that the energy transfer involved in or connected with these beats represented a gradual shift of energy from one vibration to another. As we will see in Chapter IV, this point of view was a crucial one in Schrödinger's efforts to interpret quantum mechanics in a continuous, deterministic way.

Schrödinger's second paper on wave mechanics[55] provided a derivation of the wave equation, now generalized to $3n$ dimensions, in a way that showed the "inner" connections with Hamilton's theory of mechanics

---

[53] Schrödinger's mathematical reference is to a text by L. Schlesinger, *Einführung in die Theorie der Differentialgleichungen* (Leipzig: G. J. Göschen, 1900); Schrödinger gives personal thanks to Hermann Weyl for guidance in these matters.

[54] The indefiniteness of frequency associated with the arbitrariness of the zero of energy continues in quantum theory to be either a puzzling matter or a meaningless question, depending upon one's point of view.

[55] *Ann. Physik*, **79** (1926), 489–527; received by the editor Feb. 23, 1926; *AW*, pp. 16–55; *WM*, pp. 13–40. Three later accounts of this development, more or less simplified, were given by Schrödinger: "An Undulatory Theory of the Mechanics of Atoms and Molecules," *Phys. Rev.*, **28** (1926), 1049–1070; "The Fundamental Idea of Wave Mechanics," Nobel Address, Stockholm, Dec. 12, 1933, reprinted in *STM*, pp. 166–192, and in German in *WN*, pp. 86–101; *Four Lectures on Wave Mechanics* (London: Blackie and Sons, 1928), trans. into German as *Vier Vorlesungen über Wellenmechanik* (Berlin: J. Springer, 1928), lectures given on March 5, 7, 12, and 14, 1928.

and bore out completely de Broglie's conjecture that Newtonian and wave mechanics bear the same relation to each other as do ray and wave optics. Let us consider a simplified version of his derivation.

We assume the mechanical system to be described by a set of coordinates q_i. A point in the $3n$-dimensional q-space whose coordinates are the q_i is called the "image point" of the system. Its motion as time goes on represents the "orbit" predicted by classical mechanics. Schrödinger defined this space to be non-Euclidean, with a metric derived from the expression for kinetic energy. Assuming that some type of "normal" coordinates is used and that V does not depend on velocities or momenta, we can write for twice the kinetic energy

$$2T = \sum_i A_i \dot{q}_i^2 = \sum_i p_i^2 / A_i, \tag{13}$$

since by the Lagrangean relation $p_i = \partial L(q_1, \ldots, q_{3n}; \dot{q}_1, \ldots, \dot{q}_{3n}) / \partial \dot{q}_i$ we have $p_i = A_i \dot{q}_i$. The A_i are the masses in either a conventional or generalized sense; in the latter case, they may depend on the q_i's. The length ds associated with a set of differentials $dq_1 \cdots dq_{3n}$ is then defined by

$$ds^2 = 2T \, dt^2 = \sum_i A_i \, dq_i^2. \tag{14}$$

With this definition, the speed of the image point becomes

$$v = ds/dt = (2T)^{1/2} = (2E - 2V)^{1/2}, \tag{15a}$$

which, in case V depends only on the q_i's, is the same for all directions of motion at a given point of the space. The component of v in the ith direction is clearly

$$v_i = A_i^{1/2} \dot{q}_i. \tag{15b}$$

The Hamilton–Jacobi equation may be written in terms of T and the time-dependent function W given by

$$W = -Et + S(q_1, \ldots, q_{3n}; E, P_2, \ldots, P_{3n}). \tag{16}$$

We obtain

$$2T\left(q_1, \ldots, q_{3n}; \frac{\partial W}{\partial q_1}, \cdots, \frac{\partial W}{\partial q_{3n}}\right) = 2(E - V) = \sum_i \frac{1}{A_i}\left(\frac{\partial W}{\partial q_i}\right)^2. \tag{17a}$$

It is readily seen by eq. (14) that the ith component of the gradient of W in q-space is $A_i^{-1/2}\, \partial W/\partial q_i$ so that (17a) may be rewritten

$$|\mathbf{grad}\ W|^2 = |\mathbf{grad}\ S|^2 = 2(E - V). \tag{17b}$$

If we solve this equation for the function S, we can obtain a family of surfaces in q-space by choosing fixed values for $E_1, P_2, \ldots, P_{3n}$ and setting S equal to a succession of different constants. Equation (17b) allows us to calculate a surface in the neighborhood of any given one with which we start. The value of W will change on each surface as time passes in accordance with eq. (16). Alternatively, we may think of a surface $W = $ const. moving from one to another of surfaces $S = $ const. as time goes on. Such a moving surface we will call a wave front in q-space.

A ray or wave normal is a vector with components proportional to those of $\mathbf{grad}\ W = \mathbf{grad}\ S$. By the transformation equation

$$p_k = \partial S(q_1, \ldots, q_{3n}; P_1, \ldots, P_{3n})/\partial q_k$$

such a vector is the one with components

$$\frac{p_k}{A_k^{1/2}} = \frac{1}{A_k^{1/2}} \frac{\partial S}{\partial q_k} = A_k^{1/2} \dot{q}_k. \tag{18}$$

These are just the velocity components (15b), so the wave normal has the direction of motion of the image point. Classical mechanics thus becomes the ray optics of a set of moving wave fronts in q-space.[56]

It is noted that the velocity u of the wave fronts is by no means the same as the velocity v of the image point. In fact,

$$u = \frac{|\partial W/\partial t|}{|\mathbf{grad}\ W|} = \frac{E}{(2E - 2V)^{1/2}}. \tag{19}$$

So far nothing has been said about wave length or frequency. The analogy between classical mechanics and ray optics becomes complete if the wave length is assumed to be so small that diffraction effects are negligible, and optical propagation is strictly along rays, i.e., geometrical. It then becomes natural and straightforward to introduce wave mechanics by assuming that the wave propagation picture remains accurate as the wave length takes on a magnitude comparable with the dimensions of the experimental situation, with the ray picture becoming less and less accurate.

[56] This way of describing mechanics had actually been used by Hamilton. See F. Klein, *Gesammelte Mathematische Abhandlungen* (Berlin: J. Springer, 1922), II, pp. 601–602, and references given there.

The Development of Wave Mechanics

To proceed with wave mechanics, it is necessary to introduce a wave function of oscillatory character, the phase of which is proportional to the function W. The coefficient of proportionality that leads to agreement with the previous results of quantum theory is $2\pi/h$, so we have, for instance, a function

$$\sin\left(\frac{2\pi W}{h} + \text{const.}\right) = \sin\left(\frac{-2\pi Et}{h} + \frac{2\pi S}{h} + \text{const.}\right). \tag{20}$$

We obtain, of course, $\nu = E/h$. With eq. (19) and the elementary relation $u = \lambda\nu$, we can also find the wave length λ:

$$\lambda = \frac{u}{\nu} = \frac{h}{(2E - 2V)^{1/2}}. \tag{21}$$

The frequency depends on the zero reference for energy, but the wave length in q-space does not.

Furthermore, the group velocity, which we can find from eq. (4), turns out to be exactly v as given by eq. (15a). The connection between wave propagation and particle mechanics becomes even closer if we consider the motion of a wave packet or group of waves of nearly the same frequency (value of E) and direction (values of $P_2, \ldots, P_{3n}$). Consider a group of waves all of which have the same value of W at a point $\mathscr{P}$ in q-space at time t_0, but which have values of $E, P_2, \ldots, P_{3n}$ varying over narrow ranges in the neighborhood of some fixed set of values. The speeds and directions of the different wave fronts are all different.

The assertion that these waves form a group amounts to saying that a short time t later, there will be another point $\mathscr{Q}$ at which they all have a common, but in general a new, value of W. That is, as t increases and $\mathscr{Q}$ moves, $\partial W/\partial t$ is the same for all members of the group. The value of $\partial W/\partial t$ must remain constant as the parameters $E(= P_1), P_2, \ldots, P_{3n}$ are varied over the specified range. This means that

$$\frac{\partial^2 W}{\partial t\, \partial P_k} = 0; \quad k = 1, 2, \ldots, 3n \tag{22}$$

or

$$\frac{\partial W(t)}{\partial P_k} = \frac{\partial W(t_0)}{\partial P_k} = \text{const.}; \quad k = 1, 2, \ldots, 3n. \tag{23}$$

These $3n$ equations are enough to determine the $3n$ coordinates of $\mathscr{Q}$ as functions of t, so that indeed we have a group or wave packet with a single moving point of phase agreement.

55

It is known from Hamilton–Jacobi mechanics that the condition that $\partial W/\partial P_k$ be constant solves the mechanical problem—that is, gives correctly the variation of the q_k's with time. This means that the point $\mathcal{D}$ of phase agreement is, in fact, the image point for the classical-mechanical system. A group of waves will simulate a Newtonian system as long as the group is not so broad that its place of phase agreement has little meaning for the location of the group as a whole. Schrödinger does not make any reference to the now well-known fact that quantum-mechanical wave packets always spread out in time (with a single important exception, to be mentioned shortly). The failure was emphasized by Born[57] in his criticism of Schrödinger's interpretation of the wave function.

It is still necessary to obtain a wave equation for the propagation of waves in q-space. Schrödinger takes the simple classical wave equation for this space,

$$\text{div } \mathbf{grad}\, \psi = \sum_i \frac{1}{A_i} \frac{\partial^2 \psi}{\partial q_i^2} = \frac{1}{u^2} \frac{\partial^2 \psi}{\partial t^2}, \tag{24}$$

assumes that ψ depends on the time through a factor $\exp 2\pi i \nu t$, and replaces ν/u by its value given in eq. (21), obtaining

$$\text{div } \mathbf{grad}\, \psi + \frac{8\pi^2}{h^2} (E - V)\psi = 0, \tag{25}$$

which is Schrödinger's equation for a system of n particles.[58] (He points out that the div **grad** operator may be generalized, but he does not pursue the matter.) Again the natural boundary conditions automatically bring in quantum conditions.

The function ψ no longer represents waves in ordinary three-dimensional space, so that de Broglie's ideas have essentially been left behind. Furthermore, the waves *are* the system, rather than being *guides* for it. It is to be noted, however, that no rule for obtaining the electron density or the probability of localizing a particle has been introduced.

The rest of the second paper on wave mechanics worked out results for the harmonic oscillator, the rotator with fixed axis, the rigid rotator with free axis, and the diatomic molecule (vibrating rotator), results that can be found in many modern textbooks. In particular, straightforward explanations appeared for the empirical need to use the half-integral quantum numbers that were mentioned earlier.

[57] *Z. Physik*, **40** (1926/7), 167–192.

[58] The "masses" A_i enter the operator div **grad** because of the metric given in eq. (14).

Schrödinger's next achievement[59] was to show for the special case of the simple harmonic or "Planck" oscillator that a suitable superposition of states produces a wave packet whose center exactly follows the laws of classical mechanics for such an oscillator. The superposition is made possible by a clever use of the generating function for the Hermite polynomials that appear in the theory of the oscillator.[60]

The spreading property of most wave packets appears here only as a periodic variation of the wavelike structure—the "corrugation" as Schrödinger called it. He recognized that this behavior depends on the fact that the energy levels are equally spaced, so that the frequencies are all multiples of the fundamental. However, not yet aware that this behavior is quite singular, he believed that he had given an example of a general property of continuous transition from micro- to macro-mechanics when many states of high quantum numbers are superposed.

The best and simplest description of the relation of quantum and classical mechanics is that of Ehrenfest,[61] who showed that the "center of gravity" of a wave packet—i.e., the point whose coordinates are the mean values of x, y, and z—will move with an acceleration given by the mean value of the force ($\mathbf{F} = -\mathbf{grad}\, V$) divided by the mass. For macroscopic objects, the spreading of the wave packet is negligible; both Schrödinger's general and specific comparisons were correct. However, he was clearly wrong in believing that wave packets may be formed that correspond to electrons circulating in orbits, for these would spread over the entire atom in a time of the order of n revolutions, where n is the mean radial quantum number.[62]

Not quite two months after Schrödinger started his series in the *Annalen der Physik*, he submitted papers[63] showing in detail that his system was logically equivalent to the matrix mechanics which had evolved in such a very different way and which seemed on the surface to be so utterly different. In June, 1926, before this paper had appeared, Eckart published an article in *The Physical Review* which demonstrated the same thing,[64]

---

[59] *Naturwissenschaften*, **28** (1926), 664–666; *WM*, pp. 41–44; *AW*, pp. 56–61.

[60] See, for instance, D. Bohm, *Quantum Theory* (Englewood Cliffs, New Jersey: Prentice Hall, 1951), pp. 306–308.

[61] P. Ehrenfest, *Z. Physik*, **45** (1927), 455–457.

[62] An interesting if not conclusive discussion on this point was carried on in correspondence between Schrödinger and H. A. Lorentz. See K. Przibram, ed., *Briefe zur Wellenmechanik* (Vienna: J. Springer, 1963), pp. 41–67.

[63] *Ann. Physik*, **79** (1926), 734–756; *WM*, pp. 45–61; *AW*, pp. 62–84.

[64] C. Eckart, *Phys. Rev.*, **28** (1926), 711–726.

starting, however, from the matrix point of view. The essence of the demonstration was that matrices of Heisenberg's type can be generated from any set of orthogonal functions by integrals of the form

$$G_{mn} = \int \psi_m{}^*(q)\mathbf{G}\psi_n(q)\ d\tau \tag{26}$$

where **G** signifies an operator associated with the physical quantity under consideration (p_k or q_k or some function of either or both). Eckart drew the operator concept from Born and Wiener,[65] but Schrödinger evidently came upon the idea independently.

Heisenberg's equations of motion can be satisfied by using as the set of orthogonal functions those that arise from the solution of Schrödinger's equation for the energy eigenvalues and eigenfunctions. Furthermore, if the set of matrices is given by use of Heisenberg's method, all the moments of the Schrödinger functions are known, at least in principle, and the functions themselves are thus determined. The most useful aspect of the new relationship is the ease with which selection rules and relative intensities of spectral lines can be determined from the dipole-moment matrix element formulas using Schrödinger's functions, the formulas that are, in fact, now in general use.

With the establishment of the relation between wave and matrix mechanics, Schrödinger's work became an integral part of the mainstream of quantum theory, a stream that ran rapidly and smoothly as more and more results came out. The full history of this period will only be written after much work has been done in collecting correspondence and personal reminiscences to round out the already enormous body of published literature.[66]

The year 1926 marked the productive period of Schrödinger's participation in the development of quantum physics in the strict sense (as opposed to the more philosophical area of interpretation). From then until 1932 he made a few more contributions, but in their totality they did not approach in importance the work of that one year.

Schrödinger's continuing interest after 1926 lay in two essentially

---

[65] See ref. 20, p. 42.

[66] The American Institute of Physics project, "Sources for the History of Quantum Physics," is now making such a collection. For an earlier study, see the brief, clear, and informative account by W. Heisenberg, "The Development of the Interpretation of the Quantum Theory" in *Niels Bohr and the Development of Physics,* W. Pauli, ed. (New York: McGraw-Hill and London: Pergamon, 1955), pp. 12–29.

philosophical questions: whether the wave function is to be taken as representing a real physical entity, and whether a fully continuous theory of quantum mechanics is possible. The root elements of his affirmative answers to these questions are to be found in the 1926 papers, and he continued to develop them in later interpretive writings, up to his last paper in 1958 (see Ch. IV).

Schrödinger's contributions in 1926 to the physics of quantum mechanics are all to be found in the papers of the published collection.[67] In the third paper of the basic series,[68] he presented for the first time the elegant and now familiar steady-state perturbation theory, which allows the approximate calculation of the eigenstates of a system whose potential differs by a relatively weak addition from that of a system which can be solved exactly. A feature of particular importance in this theory is the way in which a perturbation may remove degeneracy (the existence of two or more different eigenfunctions for the same eigenvalue).

In this article, Schrödinger applied perturbation theory to the Stark effect in atomic hydrogen—the effect of a steady applied electric field in modifying the Lyman and Balmer series of spectral lines. Transition intensities, as well as line-shifts, were calculated and shown to be generally in agreement with experiment. At about the same time, similar results were obtained by Epstein,[69] who worked to second order instead of first, but used a specialized method involving hypergeometric expansions, rather than the general perturbation theory introduced by Schrödinger. Several other authors also obtained results on the Stark effect.[70]

Many years later, Schrödinger referred to the calculation of the Stark effect as the "earliest quantitative achievement of wave mechanics"[71] and pointed out a limitation on the perturbation calculation that Lanczos[72] had shown in 1930: An external electric field may be small

---

[67] *AW* and *WM*; see ref. 51.

[68] *Ann. Physik*, **80** (1926), 437–490; *WM*, pp. 62–101; *AW*, pp. 85–138.

[69] P. S. Epstein, *Phys. Rev.*, **28** (1926) 695–710. This paper appeared in the same issue as that of Eckhart, ref. 64.

[70] W. Pauli, Jr. (*Z. Physik*, **36** (1926), 336–363) obtained the line shifts to first order using matrix mechanics; G. Wentzel (*Z. Physik*, **38** (1926), 518–529) and I. Waller (*Z. Physik*, **38** (1926), 635–646) obtained the shifts to second order. Wentzel followed Schrödinger and used what is now often called the WKB method; Waller worked independently of Schrödinger by a method similar to that of Einstein. None of these authors, however, dealt with intensities.

[71] "Are There Quantum Jumps?" *Brit. J. Phil. Sci.*, **3** (1952), 109–123 and 233–247; reprinted in *WIL*, pp. 132–160. Quoted from *WIL*, p. 152.

[72] C. Lanczos, *Z. Physik*, **62** (1930), 518–544.

compared to the nuclear field in the neighborhood of the nucleus; but at points far from the nucleus where its own field is weak, the relative perturbation by the external field is strong. The consequence is a line broadening, especially in the higher members of the series.

In a fourth paper[73] concerning the problem of time-dependent perturbations, Schrödinger began by eliminating E from eq. (25), going to a fourth order real equation, and then showing that a simpler result is obtained if one is willing to use a complex equation. Using the expression (25) in which the masses of the particles are included in the differential operator expression, one can write

$$\text{div } \mathbf{grad } \psi - \frac{8\pi^2 V}{h^2} \psi + \frac{4\pi i}{h} \frac{\partial \psi}{\partial t} = 0 \qquad (27)$$

as the original form of Schrödinger's time-dependent equation. (I have chosen the sign of the term with $\partial \psi / \partial t$ in accordance with later convention.)

This equation was taken as the starting point for the study of dispersion, i.e., the absorption and reradiation of incident light of an arbitrary frequency ν. Schrödinger gave a special treatment of the resonance case, when ν is equal to one of the characteristic difference frequencies of the atom, $(E_n - E_m)/h$.[74] The possibility of the radiation of frequencies equal to $\nu \pm (E_n - E_m)/h$, already predicted by Smekal and calculated by Kramers and Heisenberg[75] on the basis of the older quantum theory, was worked out in detail.

The article concluded with a statement of the generalization of the wave equation to the relativistic domain and a statement of the equation of continuity applied to $\psi \psi^*$. The former (in one or another equivalent form) was published almost simultaneously by several other authors[76] and is generally called the "Klein–Gordon–Schrödinger" scalar relativistic equation. The equation of continuity (found also, e.g., by

[73] *Ann. Physik*, **81** (1926), 109–139; *WM*, pp. 102–123; *AW*, pp. 139–169.

[74] See, for instance, the treatment of these effects in D. Bohm, *op. cit.*, Ch. 18.

[75] A. Smekal, *Naturwissenschaften*, **11** (1923), 873–875; H. A. Kramers and W. Heisenberg, *Z. Physik*, **31** (1925), 681–708. Transitions of this sort were first discovered by C. V. Raman, *Indian J. Phys.*, **2** (March, 1928); *Nature*, **121** (1928), 501–502 and **122** (1928), 12–13.

[76] O. Klein, *Z. Physik*, **37** (1926), 895–906; V. Fock, *Z. Physik*, **38** (1926), 242–250 and **39** (1926), 226–232; J. Kudar, *Ann. Physik*, **81** (1926), 632; W. Gordon, *Z. Physik*, **40** (1926), 117–133; Th. de Donder and Fr. H. van den Dungen, *Comptes Rendues*, **183** (1926), 22–24; L. de Broglie, *Comptes Rendues*, **183** (1926), 272–274.

Gordon)[77] was interpreted by Schrödinger as indicating a flow and conservation of "real" electron charge, but has since been taken generally to mean the flow and conservation of probability.

The next paper[78] in the collected works is a brief remark on the Compton effect. Schrödinger showed that if we consider a steady state of ingoing and outgoing waves for both electron and photon, the results for change of direction, momentum, and energy, usually obtained with a corpuscular theory, come out immediately if we treat the scattering as a Bragg type of reflection based on constructive interference. Either wave may be considered to be reflected on the "grating" formed by the interference pattern produced by the combination of ingoing and outgoing waves of the other. This calculation exemplifies the usual steady-state procedure followed in scattering problems, but it is not correct quantum-mechanically, since it treats two waves interacting in three-dimensional space instead of the proper six dimensions.

The next paper, on the conservation of energy and momentum,[79] is one that, when viewed in retrospect, turns out to have been unfruitful. Schrödinger attempted to extend the conservation theorems of classical electromagnetic theory to the charge-current vector which he had earlier found for the one-particle wave function. He was, in fact, able to find a theorem which satisfied him that the interaction of electrons with electromagnetic radiation can be brought in without the necessity of quantizing the latter. He granted that the theory was in disagreement with observations that showed a discontinuous transfer of energy and that it did not properly handle the problem of the self-field of an electron. But he apparently did not see what Dirac pointed out shortly afterwards,[80] that he was confusing here the ψ-field with de Broglie waves, since his theorem only applied to a three-dimensional description. Dirac's article developed a method (the so-called "second quantization") for quantizing the electromagnetic field and treating interactions with a system of charges that avoided the dimensional difficulty, although it did not yet provide a proper form for the conservation laws. The latter had to await the development of relativistic quantum electrodynamics.[81]

[77] W. Gordon, see ref. 76.

[78] *Ann. Physik*, **82** (1927), 257–264; *WM*, pp. 124–129; *AW*, pp. 170–177.

[79] *Ann. Physik*, **82** (1927), 265–272; *WM*, pp. 130–136; *AW*, pp. 178–185.

[80] P. A. M. Dirac, *Proc. Roy. Soc.* (London), **114A** (1927), 243–265.

[81] See, for example, N. N. Bogoliubov and D. V. Shirkov, *Introduction to the Theory of Quantized Fields*, trans. G. M. Volkoff (New York: Interscience, 1959), Ch. VI.

Schrödinger returned to the many-dimensional wave mechanics in the last paper of the collection, to work out explicitly his proposal that energy transfer be regarded as occurring continuously between different proper vibrations.[82] He used the time-dependent perturbation theory that he and others had already developed, applying it to a combined system consisting of two lightly coupled separate systems with pairs of energy levels of the same energy difference. That is, we assume that the first system has the levels E_k and E_l, and the second has levels E_m' and E_n', that are related by

$$E_k - E_l = E_m' - E_n' > 0$$

Then a level for the combined system with energy $E = E_k + E_n'$, is degenerate, since

$$E = E_k + E_n' = E_l + E_m'. \tag{28}$$

Time-dependent perturbation theory shows that if the system at $t = 0$ is in the first combined level, i.e., if the unprimed system is in the higher level E_k and the primed system is in the lower level E_n', after a certain time the system will be in the other state. In fact, there will be an oscillation or exchange between the two states. No additional "quantum postulate" is needed to account for this transfer (such as the assertion that the first system undergoes a downward "jump," emitting a quantum of energy which is then absorbed by the other in an abrupt upward transition). We may say that the two systems undergo a resonance phenomenon resembling beats in acoustics, and thus we may describe the results in terms of resonant frequencies without referring to energies. In this case, the frequency of transfer depends on the perturbation and is the difference between the frequencies E/h for the two orthogonal states resulting from the removal of the degeneracy by the perturbation.

In place of reference to initial and final energies, we have reference to the amplitudes of the different excited states. In fact, Schrödinger extended his considerations to statistical aggregates of similar systems, all with the same sets of levels and level differences, and showed how to relate these amplitudes to the weights used in statistical thermodynamics. In this way, he obtained a correct expression for the entropy of such an aggregate. Finally, he pointed out that the same result can be obtained using Born's statistical interpretation of ψ, but stated that he preferred to

[82] E. Schrödinger, *Ann. Physik*, **83** (1927), 956–968; *WM*, pp. 137–146; *AW*, pp. 186–198.

avoid the latter because it does not help in understanding the statistics of thermodynamics, irreversibility, etc.

Schrödinger's next contribution to quantum mechanics was a lucid, largely pedagogical, basic discussion of line widths and resonance.[83] Perhaps because the connection was not worked out in detail between the one-dimensional example he used and the actual cases for which this example was a model, the article has apparently been overlooked.[84] It deals with one-dimensional step potentials, particularly with relations of amplitude and phase for a wave function in two regions of oscillation (classically accessible) separated by a "sill" or classically inaccessible potential barrier. By means of a clear and elegant method of describing these relations, Schrödinger showed that eigenfunctions group themselves into those whose amplitudes are large on the left, and vice versa. Then he was able to discuss the case of resonance or near-resonance that occurs if two almost separated similar valleys are connected by a wide barrier which may be allowed to shrink. In this way the exchange phenomenon, first described by Hund,[85] can be easily treated. The peculiar phenomenon of a one-dimensional system "resisting" degeneration appears here.[86] As a parameter of the system is varied so that two eigenvalues "belonging" to the respective valleys approach each other, they never "cross," but may exchange their roles of having their eigenfunctions large on the right or left sides of the barrier.

Finally, Schrödinger considered the case in which the right-hand "valley" is extended to infinity. As the valley's width increases, it acquires more and more eigenvalues, leading to the continuous spectrum of the unbounded system. A whole "army" of successive eigenvalues from the right "attack" those on the left. The result is that those on the left appear to be "washed-out" lines. There is the appearance of a condensation of continuous levels around the now "virtual" levels of the left-hand valley.[87]

Schrödinger showed how to normalize the continuous eigenfunctions

[83] *S. B. Preuss. Akad. Wiss.* (1929), 668–682.

[84] For instance, no reference is given to this work in the fairly extensive bibliography of Robert G. Breene, *The Shift and Shape of Spectral Lines* (Oxford: Pergamon Press, 1961).

[85] F. Hund, *Z. Physik,* **40** (1926/7), 742–764.

[86] First described by J. von Neumann and E. Wigner, *Physik. Z.,* **30** (1939), 467–470.

[87] This effect is undoubtedly the same as the Stark broadening discussed by Lanczos. See ref. 72.

and, if one wishes, to introduce a weight function to describe this "condensation." He then conjectured that an atomic system which can give up energy from any of its higher levels is analogous to this one-dimensional system composed of a rectangular well coupled to a continuum. The coupling may, for instance, be by means of a weak external perturbation coupling the internal variables to the center-of-mass system. Thus this analogy can be used to describe line width. The relation of line width to lifetime may be established if one constructs a wave packet of eigenfunctions for a narrow band of energies near one of the "maxima" in the spectrum. Such a wave packet may at time zero be nearly all contained within the well, but as time goes on, the differing frequencies will upset the destructive interference outside the well, and the wave will "leak" through the barrier.[88]

A basic theorem of quantum mechanics is that relating the uncertainties (root-mean-square deviations expected in a series of repeated observations on the same state) for two conjugate variables. Schrödinger developed the generalization of this theorem,[89] extending even further the generalizations obtained by Condon[90] and Robertson.[91] The theorem he proved reads

$$(\Delta \mathbf{A})^2 (\Delta \mathbf{B})^2 \geq |\tfrac{1}{2}(\overline{\mathbf{AB} + \mathbf{BA}}) - \overline{\mathbf{A}}\overline{\mathbf{B}}|^2 + |\tfrac{1}{2}(\overline{\mathbf{AB} - \mathbf{BA}})|^2 \qquad (29)$$

for any two Hermitian operators **A** and **B**. Schrödinger then went on to describe the considerations on wave packet spreading that led him to this result.[92] In particular, he made use of what he called the "*q*-number method," which is now commonly referred to as the Heisenberg representation, in which time dependence appears in operators rather than in wave functions.

The same representation was applied by Schrödinger in deriving a fundamental property of the Dirac electron in free space,[93] the so-called *Zitterbewegung.* He started with the Hamiltonian

$$H = c\alpha_1 p_1 + c\alpha_2 p_2 + c\alpha_3 p_3 + \alpha_4 mc^2, \qquad (30)$$

[88] See the general discussion, with literature references, in E. C. Kemble, *Fundamental Principles of Quantum Mechanics* (New York: McGraw-Hill, 1937), sec. 31, pp. 172–195.

[89] *S. B. Preuss. Akad. Wiss.* (1930), 296–303; received June 15, 1930.

[90] E. U. Condon, *Science,* **69** (1929), 573–574.

[91] H. P. Robertson, *Phys. Rev.,* **34** (1929), 163–164.

[92] These results are readily available in texts on quantum mechanics. See, for example, E. Merzbacher, *Quantum Mechanics* (New York: John Wiley, 1961), Ch. 8, problem 9, p. 165.

[93] *S. B. Preuss. Akad. Wiss.* (1930), 418–428; received July 17, 1930.

and used Breit's interpretation[94] in accordance with which $c\alpha_1$, $c\alpha_2$, and $c\alpha_3$ correspond to the velocity components v_x, v_y, and v_z, and α_4 corresponds to $(1 - \beta^2)^{1/2}$. It must be noted that the velocity and momentum components do not have here the simple relation they have in classical mechanics. The α_i are, of course, represented as 4×4 Dirac matrices, with the matrix indices or subscripts representing a fifth variable, not to be confused with the index enumerating space and time components.

Using operator calculus, Schrödinger derived the operator relation

$$dx_k/dt = c\alpha_k \tag{31}$$

which bears out the correspondence indicated. However, since the α's obey the matrix equation $\alpha_k^2 = 1$, we have the pecularity that the square (in the operator sense) of every velocity component is c^2. This means that every measurement of velocity in a given direction must yield the values $\pm c$; an average value much smaller than c can only appear as a mean of many positive and negative readings each equal in magnitude to c. The situation is clarified by an expansion by which the operator x_k is written as the sum of two terms, one of which varies linearly with the time, having a coefficient implying a velocity that corresponds to p_k/m. The other term has an almost periodic character with a velocity corresponding to $c\alpha_k$, and represents a kind of rapid fine-scale oscillation or *Zitterbewegung*. The amplitude of this motion is shown to be of the order of the Compton wave length $h/4\pi mc$, about 10^{-11} cm. Schrödinger also derived some relationships between these linear oscillations and similar oscillations of the spin moment (transverse to the direction of motion), but their meaning was not altogether clear. He presented the entire affair as a matter of considerable interest but of uncertain ultimate value.

Schrödinger's calculation has, however, turned out to be of basic importance for the theory of the Dirac electron. Foldy and Wouthuysen[95] developed a canonical transformation that made the comparison of relativistic and nonrelativistic electron theories straightforward, and in so doing introduced a new operator, which they called the mean position operator. The ordinary position operator then appears to undergo trembling motion with respect to the new one, just as Schrödinger demonstrated. However, this motion cannot be observed, because any

[94] G. Breit, *Proc. Nat. Acad. Sci.*, **14** (1928), 553–559.

[95] L. L. Foldy and S. Wouthuysen, *Phys. Rev.*, **78** (1950), 29–36. A summary is given by L. L. Foldy in "Relativistic Wave Equations" in *Quantum Theory*, D. R. Bates, ed. (New York: Academic Press, 1962), III, 11–23.

attempt to make observation to within a Compton wave length would involve energies and momenta large enough to create electron-positron pairs. The one-particle state being observed would thus be lost.

The *Zitterbewegung* turns out to be related to interference between positive and negative electron energy states. However, Schrödinger was unable to come to this understanding because the meaning of the negative energy states was not comprehended at the time—electron-positron pair production was not discovered until two years later. Schrödinger worked for some time during those two years in what turned out to be a wrong direction, trying to modify Dirac theory to remove the negative-energy difficulty, largely by removing the possibility of transfers between positive and negative energy states. Two of his papers in the *Berliner Berichte* bear on this attempt.[96]

Although these efforts were abortive, they did allow him to point out the difficulties involved in giving time and space an equal footing for the purpose of combining quantum theory and relativity. Quantum theory initially had space and time on quite different bases—position as a quantized observable, time as a uniformly progressing independent variable. This problem has since been solved in covariantly formulated quantum electrodynamics, as presented in many standard texts.

Two short contributions and one substantial set of papers deserve mention in concluding this account. With two colleagues, Schrödinger published a theoretical addendum to an experimental paper on the Stark effect with sudden changes of field[97] which showed that the Stark pattern of a spectrum would, surprisingly, show up in the order of one period. After writing a paper on the proper vibrations of a spherical space,[98] Schrödinger was led to consider the basic question of the single-valuedness of the wave function, showing it to be possible and consistent that in place of single-valuedness there be a double-valuedness corresponding to a change of sign, arising by a type of two-Riemann-sheet structure of wave function configuration space.[99]

Schrödinger's last substantial contribution to wave mechanics was

[96] *S. B. Preuss. Akad. Wiss.* (1931), 63–72 and 238–247. Schrödinger reviewed his work in relativistic electron theory in *Ann. Inst. Henri Poincaré*, **2** (1932), 269–310.

[97] H. R. von Traubenberg, R. Gebauer, and E. Schrödinger, *Z. Physik*, **78** (1932), 309–317.

[98] *Acta Pontif. Acad. Sci.*, **2** (1937), 321–364.

[99] E. Schrödinger, *Ann. Physik*, **32** (1938), 49–55.

the elegant factorization method for obtaining eigenvalues and eigen-functions for stationary state problems.[100] This method, useful only for certain potentials of convenient form, involves the introduction of first-order differential operators that, in a sense, "factor" the basic Schrö-dinger equation and allow the generation of a set of eigenvalues and eigenfunctions in step-wise fashion, referred to frequently as a "ladder."

Quantum mechanics is also involved in Schrödinger's work in space-time structure and meson theory, but consideration of these matters would take us too far afield. We turn now to the interesting and difficult problems of interpretation.

[100] *Proc. R. Irish Acad.*, **46**A (1940), 9–16, **46**A (1941), 183–206, and **47**A (1941), 53–54.

Chapter IV

Schrödinger's Interpretation of Quantum Mechanics

1. INTRODUCTION

Erwin Schrödinger held a view of quantum mechanics which was, or appeared to be, radically different from that of most of his contemporaries in theoretical physics. He attacked the notion of quantum jumps, those discontinuous transitions that defy any space-time description yet seem to be implied by a wealth of experimental evidence. He expressed considerable dissatisfaction with the statistical interpretation of the wave function that Max Born introduced. On some occasions he even seemed to deny the existence of the particles themselves.

Throughout his life Schrödinger was committed to the ideal of a rational and realistic theory of events in the atomic world. In an obituary notice, Max Born described the tenor of Schrödinger's thought as essentially classical, as the hope of finding "the way back to the classical physics of clearly comprehensible events" (*den Weg zur klassischen Physik der anschaulich erfassbaren Vorgänge zurückzufinden*).[1] How are we to understand this attitude on the part of a man who called the statistical heritage of Boltzmann his "first love in science,"[2] who perceived from his teacher Exner that classical physics itself has a statistical foundation in the very notion of atomism,[3] and who played such a prominent role in the revolution that overthrew classical physics and brought the new quantum mechanics into a place of dominance?

Three ways of approaching this question suggest themselves. The most representative and complete single presentation of Schrödinger's views on the interpretation of quantum mechanics[4] might be subjected to an

[1] M. Born, *Physikalische Blätter*, **17** (1961), 85–87.
[2] See Ch. II, p. 15. [3] See Ch. II, pp. 30–33.
[4] The best choice seems to be Schrödinger's article "Are There Quantum Jumps?," *WIL*, pp. 132–160.

68

exhaustive analysis. Or all the available records—correspondence, note-books, personal reports of private discussions and public meetings, details of his private life, and all of Schrödinger's published writings— might be examined in search of a definitive and comprehensive view of the man and his views. The third alternative, more limited but appropri-ate to the scope of the present work, is to examine each of the published writings, correlating the various lines of thought represented in them. In this way, one may hope to distinguish Schrödinger's basic ideas from those which were transitory or colored by the particular occasion of their expression. Although a picture derived in this way cannot be so complete as one that takes into account the privately available material, it may nevertheless be useful in revealing the core of his views.

2. WAVES

The central element in Schrödinger's interpretation of quantum mechanics is the wave picture based on his wave equations (12) or (25), and (27).[5] Let us attempt to describe this picture in a way as favorable to Schrödinger's interpretation as seems feasible. In this picture, a physical system is considered to be a continuum which can undergo complex modes of vibration, describable by means of a certain function of $3n$ coordinates, where n is the number of particles that would be included in the corresponding classical picture. This function has wavelike properties, a fact which is evident when only one particle is under consideration and the analogy with three-dimensional hydrodynamic waves is close, and also when the behavior of the function in $3n$-dimensional space is studied with enough mathematical imagination to provide a meaningful extension of the wave idea to such a complex system.

Every physical system has a set of normal modes or eigenvibrations. The eigenfunctions describing them are solutions of the time-independent equation (25), multiplied by a complex simple-harmonic time factor $\exp[-2\pi i E t/h]$. In this factor, E is the eigenvalue in (25), associated with the given eigenfunction. While it is commonly identified with energy in the macroscopic sense, Schrödinger suggested[6] that the

---

[5] Ch. III, pp. 52, 56, and 60.

[6] This suggestion was initially made in the first paper on wave mechanics, *Ann. Physik*, **79** (1926), 361–376 (*WM*, pp. 1–12 and *AW*, pp. 1–16), and repeated in "Might Energy be a Merely Statistical Concept?" *Nuovo Cimento*, **9** (1958), 162–170.

frequency $\nu = E/h$ is the basic physical entity. A system may be set into vibration in a single one of its modes, or it may vibrate in any linear combination or superposition of them. In case of such a superposition, there is no longer a single frequency, but instead a complex behavior in time that for nearly all systems[7] is not periodic.

A pair of systems in weak interaction which can be described with fair accuracy as almost independent will have a combined frequency ν which is the sum of the frequencies of the two separate systems:

$$\nu = \nu_1 + \nu_2. \tag{32}$$

The addition of frequencies is a nonclassical feature that is taken as a basic assumption and is not expected to be obvious. Now suppose that because of the weak interaction, an exchange occurs between two degenerate states—states of equal combined frequency. We can describe the conservation property of this exchange by writing $\nu = \nu'$ or

$$\nu_1 + \nu_2 = \nu_1{}' + \nu_2{}'. \tag{33}$$

Rearranging and multiplying by Planck's constant h, we have

$$h\nu_1 - h\nu_1{}' = h\nu_2{}' - h\nu_2, \tag{34}$$

which is the Einstein–Bohr frequency condition, usually interpreted as meaning that system 1 undergoes a quantum transition up from energy $h\nu_1{}'$ to $h\nu_1$—assuming both sides of eq. (34) to be positive—while system 2 undergoes a downward transition from a level of energy $h\nu_2{}'$ to one of energy $h\nu_2$.[8]

The specific feature of Schrödinger's view is that the transitions go on continuously in the wave process described. Both modes are present simultaneously for each system, the relative amplitudes varying as the exchange proceeds. As is well known, the rate of exchange depends on the perturbation "energy";[9] the frequency of oscillation between the two states is $\Delta E/h$, where ΔE is the difference of the "energies" of the two states that results from the perturbation. Such an oscillating process can quite properly be called "resonance."

---

[7] Exceptions are the simple harmonic oscillator and the case of the potential $V = V_0(a/x - x/a)^2$, treated, for instance, by I. I. Gol'dman and V. D. Krivchenkov, *Problems in Quantum Mechanics* (Reading, Mass.: Addison-Wesley, 1961) pp. 3 and 52–53.

[8] See the discussion of such transitions in Ch. III, pp. 62–63.

[9] See accounts of time-dependent perturbation theory, given, e.g., by D. Bohm, *Quantum Theory* (Englewood Cliffs, New Jersey: Prentice Hall, 1951), Ch. 18.

Interpretation of Quantum Mechanics

This scheme can be extended to treat the emission and absorption of radiation of a given frequency $\nu_{rad} = \nu_1 - \nu_1'$ by an assembly of like atoms or molecules in equilibrium at a high temperature. The radiation field here acts as the weak perturbation coupling all the atomic systems together.

There are many further possible extensions—in fact, the same scheme may be applied to just about any steady process that one can imagine. One assigns a quantum-mechanical frequency to any particle or system to which a definite energy is commonly ascribed. For instance, to the electrons in a beam that have fallen through a given potential V we ascribe a frequency

$$\nu = eV/h = \tfrac{1}{2}mv^2/h, \tag{35}$$

where $\tfrac{1}{2}mv^2$ is the usual (nonrelativistic) value of the kinetic energy of the electrons. If potential energy is also present, e.g., the Fermi energy of electrons in a metal, this must be included in calculating ν.

Thus the Franck–Hertz experiment may be described by saying that a beam of electrons of a pure frequency ν_2' interacts with an assembly of atoms of a pure frequency ν_1', and that by eq. (34) the electron beam acquires vibrations of frequency ν_2, while the atoms get excitation of frequency ν_1'.

The presence of the higher mode in the assembly of atoms is indicated by the resonance of this mode with emitted radiation which, in turn, indicates its frequency by its action in a spectrometer. The vacuum may be considered an electromagnetic system with frequency zero, so the frequency difference for this system is the actual radiation frequency.

The two electron-beam frequencies may be detected by a suitable "velocity" selector, which does not measure a velocity in a direct way but instead indicates the absence of deflection of a steady beam in a pair of crossed electric and magnetic fields of appropriate magnitudes.

Similarly, the photoelectric effect may be described as the excitation of a higher frequency in the electrons of the metallic surface under test, and the consequent drop of the frequency of the oncoming radiation from a given value to zero. The wave picture of the Compton effect described on p. 61 is still another example.

For all such steady-beam processes, the known experimental effects are describable by continuous wavelike processes obeying the quantum resonance rule (33), or its generalization for more than two systems

$$\nu_1 + \nu_2 + \nu_3 + \cdots + \nu_n = \nu_1' + \nu_2' + \nu_3' + \cdots + \nu_n'. \tag{36}$$

No sudden or discontinuous transitions are involved. This is the reason why Schrödinger said that quantum jumps will go the way of astronomical epicycles as outmoded, obsolete concepts.[10]

To develop the wave picture further, let us consider in more detail the electromagnetic properties of an atomic system. Schrödinger discovered,[11] after a false start,[12] that the proper expression for the charge density in a one-electron atom is $-e\psi\psi^*$, and that for a many-electron atom one can integrate over the coordinates of all but one electron and obtain a corresponding expression.[13] Using this formula, it becomes possible to write an expression for the mean electron dipole strength in an atomic system vibrating in an arbitrary superposition of normal modes. If $\psi_1, \ldots, \psi_n, \ldots$ are the eigenfunctions, a general vibration is given by

$$\psi = \sum_n c_n \psi_n \exp\left[-2\pi i \nu_n t\right]. \tag{37}$$

The mean dipole moment $\mathbf{p}_e$ of a single radiating electron is the integral

$$\mathbf{p}_e = -e \int \psi^* \mathbf{r} \psi \, d\tau, \tag{38}$$

where $d\tau$ is the appropriate volume element in $3n$-dimensional space and $\mathbf{r}$ is the vector whose components are the coordinates assigned to the electron in question. Substituting (37) into (38), we have

$$\mathbf{p}_e = -e \sum_{n,m} c_n^* c_m \exp\left[2\pi i (\nu_n - \nu_m)t\right] \int \psi_n^* \mathbf{r} \psi_m \, d\tau. \tag{39}$$

The dipole moment has oscillating components at just those frequencies known to be radiated. Thus it appears that the classical electromagnetic theory for the radiation by an oscillating electric dipole could be used, yielding radiation that satisfies the Bohr frequency condition. Single modes, corresponding to the steady states of the Bohr theory, contribute nothing to the radiation.

Furthermore, the intensity of the radiation for a given component of frequency $\nu_n - \nu_m$ is proportional to the square of the dipole matrix element $\int \psi_n^* \mathbf{r} \psi_m \, d\tau$, a result borne out by a vast amount of spectroscopic evidence concerning selection rules and relative intensities. The difficulty with using (39) for calculating radiation intensities is that it

[10] "Are There Quantum Jumps?" *WIL*, p. 135.
[11] *Ann. Physik*, **80** (1926), 437–490; *WM*, pp. 62–101; *AW*, pp. 85–138.
[12] *WM*, p. 60.
[13] *Ann. Physik*, **81** (1926), 109–139; *WM*, pp. 102–123; *AW*, pp. 139–169.

involves the amplitudes of both initial and final states,[14] whereas the formulas for the intensity of radiation from a hot gas relate emission rates to the amplitudes of the upper states and absorption rates to those in lower states. These formulas are also very well verified by much evidence.

However, even though Schrödinger's hope[15] that eq. (39) would properly describe radiation has proved incorrect, the usual time-dependent perturbation theory for both induced and spontaneous transitions gives the coefficients c_n of eq. (37) as continuous functions of the time and yields the same set of radiated frequencies. The significant fact is that a particular c_n will in general have a finite rate of increase at time $t = 0$ even if its value is zero at this time, assuming that other appropriate coefficients have appreciable values at the initial time. Thus radiation "between" two levels can occur when only one level is occupied, or as Schrödinger would say, when one mode is excited.

These two different approaches can be unified if the process called "second quantization" is carried out.[16] In this process, the coefficients c_n and $c_n{}^*$ are taken as operators which function to change the occupation numbers of given levels or modes. When the rules for these operators are established in accord with the Pauli exclusion principle, it turns out that in place of $c_n c_n{}^* c_m c_m{}^*$ that appears in the expression for the square of the dipole moment, we have the expression $N_n(1 - N_m)$, where N_n and N_m are the numbers (either 0 or 1) of electrons in the respective states denoted by n and m. Radiation occurs only when one of the levels is occupied and one empty.

This type of approach to radiation was not discussed by Schrödinger; but in 1950 he took up the concept of empty or full states, denying his earlier view of superposed modes in a single system, when he acknowledged second quantization as "the only precise formulation of the view now held."[17] (See sec. 4 below.)

---

[14] This difficulty is discussed by Ruark and Urey, *Atoms, Molecules, and Quanta* (New York: McGraw-Hill, 1930), pp. 697–698.

[15] See his articles in *Ann. Physik*, **79** (1926), 734–756, eq. (38) (*WM*, pp. 45–61, and *AW*, pp. 66–84), and *Ann. Physik*, **81** (1926), 109–139, eq. (44) (*WM*, pp. 102–123, and *AW*, pp. 139–169).

[16] J. Frenkel, *Wave Mechanics, Advanced General Theory* (New York: Oxford University Press, 1934), sec. 50; see also W. Heisenberg, *Ann. Physik*, **9** (1931), 338–346, and L. Schiff, *Quantum Mechanics* (New York: McGraw-Hill, 1955), Ch. XIII.

[17] "What is an Elementary Particle?" sec. 6, *STM*, p. 206; *WN*, p. 131.

Schrödinger gave a strong argument[18] for continuous rather than discrete transitions in atoms by considering the coherence length mentioned above in Chapter III.[19] In 1891 Michelson showed by means of a beam-splitting interferometer with arms of quite different extensions that the light whose interference was being observed would show an interference pattern with a large path difference, the upper limit of which is called the coherence length.[20] For the cadmium red line, for instance, this length is about 30 centimeters.

How are we to interpret this result in modern terms? In the first place, it was clear to Michelson, as it is clear to us today, that in all ordinary circumstances[21] the radiation from an assembly of atoms is incoherent. Each separate atom therefore must radiate wave trains that are about 30 cm. long, and a particular act of radiation will take about 30 cm/3 $\times$ 10^{10} cm/sec $= 10^{-9}$ sec or about 5×10^5 vibrations. This time is equal, in fact, to the lifetime of the state that is normally computed from the natural line width;[22] it is also comparable to the time between collisions in a gas at ordinary temperatures and, say, 0.1 atmosphere of pressure.

Such a continuous emission fits Schrödinger's wave picture very well. If we object that the waves are "really" waves of probability, and that "actually" the electron jumps down at some unknown instant, emitting a photon of energy in a very short, or even zero, interval of time, we immediately find a serious difficulty. Let us imagine using a weak light and a counter that responds to single photons—conditions under which the necessity for considering "jumps" seems inescapable. When the counter, placed at the viewing port of the interferometer, registers a photon, can we say when the jump occurred? By which path through the apparatus shall we compute the time delay? If the path difference is 30 cm, we get two answers differing by half a million periods! The concept of a jump occurring at a definite but unknown time seems to be without meaning.

The waves we have been talking about have certain general properties of importance. Regardless of one's interpretation, they influence the behavior of other objects, and insofar as the latter are called "real," so

[18] "Are There Quantum Jumps?" sec. 2, *WIL*, p. 137.

[19] Ch. III, pp. 41, 49.

[20] See M. Born and E. Wolf, *Principles of Optics* (London: Pergamon Press, 1954), pp. 318–322.

[21] That is, without stimulated emission of the sort that occurs in a maser or laser.

[22] Fourier analysis (or more elementary consideration) shows that the lifetime Δt and the line width measured as a frequency bandwidth $\Delta \nu$ obey the relation $\Delta t \, \Delta \nu \gtrsim 1$.

must the former.[23] On the other hand, they have an abstract and apparently nonclassical nature in that they have a character which calls for representation in $3n$-dimensional space.

However, this high dimensionality has a closer analogy in classical physics than is commonly supposed. The vibrations of a complex mechanical system, e.g., a helicopter rotor, are clearly real, in 3-dimensional space, yet are usually computed in terms of "normal coordinates" in a $3n$-dimensional space of Lagrangean mechanics. The conceptual difficulty lies with the word "wave," since the hydrodynamical analogy does not apply, rather than with any "nonclassical" or "nonreal" character. Schrödinger's waves have phases which require representation by complex numbers, but this fact cannot be called nonphysical because we can always use the exact equivalent of a pair of real functions in place of a simple complex one. These phases lead to the specifically wavelike behavior of interference, but in a nonclassical way because of the restriction of amplitudes involved in normalization—the constancy of the value of $\int \psi^* \psi \, d\tau$. Schrödinger never disputed any of these facts.

When ordinary Euclidean geometry is used as a basis for wave mechanics, this geometry is a structural element which is adopted on conceptual or postulational grounds, but which cannot itself be verified independently. It is conceivable that an adequate theory of atomic events will require the abandonment of ordinary geometry. This point of view was raised and discussed penetratingly by Schrödinger[24] in his response to an article on the subject by von Laue. However, no conclusions were reached calling for new geometry; Schrödinger continued to use ordinary Euclidean geometry in his later work in wave mechanics.

The coordinates that appear in the wave functions are particle coordinates. In particular, point-charge types of potential energy functions appear in the wave equations.[25] Thus a certain amount of structural

[23] Schrödinger writes in "What is an Elementary Particle?" sec. 3, *STM*, p. 198; *WN*, p. 125: "Something that influences the physical behavior of something else must not in any respect be called less real than the something it influences—whatever meaning we may give to the dangerous epithet 'real.'"

[24] *Naturwissenschaften*, **22** (1934), 518–520; M. von Laue, *Naturwissenschaften*, **22** (1934), 439.

[25] Schrödinger worried about this fact that on the one hand made the solution of the wave equation relatively easy, and on the other represented an incompleteness in the theory. See his articles in *Ann. Physik*, **79** (1926), 734–756; *WM*, pp. 45–61; *AW*, pp. 66–84; and *Ann. Physik*, **82** (1927), 265–272; *WM*, pp. 130–136; *AW*, pp. 178–185. The development of quantum electrodynamics, including second quantization (see ref. 16, p. 73), solved the difficulty much along the lines Schrödinger apparently hoped for.

detail is embodied in the wave systems. Born's assertion that for Schrö-dinger "there are no particles"[26] is thus overstated. But Schrödinger himself discussed the limitation placed by nature on structural detail, as deduced from the Heisenberg uncertainty principle.[27] The argument, which amounts to comparing the loss of detail to that in a microphotograh blurred by diffraction effects, is sound and in accordance with the usual discussions of the Heisenberg principle.

However, a quantitative extension of this idea to the question of how much information is contained in the wave function is open to doubt. In his long 1935 review article,[28] Schrödinger described our inability to specify fully the state of a system at a given time by saying that only one-half as many variables can be specified as in the classical case. That is, we may specify the positions of all the particles, but then cannot specify the momenta. This statement is correct, but since specifying positions means giving a set of values for $\psi\psi^*$, it fails to point out that phases may also be determined.[29] It is not with regard to the total amount of specifi-able information that quantum mechanics differs from classical mechanics, but with regard to the type of prediction that can be deduced from the information.

Another property of waves is that their over-all form or *Gestalt* appears to be a more basic property than it would for a collection of particles. Schrödinger pointed this out for the influence of an optical wave train on a photosensitive surface.[30] The relevant frequencies for the photo-electric threshold appear only as Fourier components, and not as immediately obvious particulars, such as amplitude or rate of change. An atomic system has even more the character of a *Gestalt*. The primacy of this concept was stressed in his 1950 lectures, "Science and Hum-anism,"[31] with remarks about "pure shape" that call for some criticism.

Any entity, when perceived as a *Gestalt*, is known by means of par-ticulars of which we are aware only in the sense that we rely on them in

---

[26] M. Born, *Brit. Journ. Phil. of Sci.*, **4** (1953/4), 95–106. Modified form of "The Interpretation of Quantum Mechanics," a speech given Dec. 8, 1952.

[27] "Conceptual Models in Physics and Their Philosophical Value," address delivered before the Physical Society of Frankfort-on-Main, Dec. 8, 1928, *STM,* p. 156.

[28] *Naturwissenschaften*, **23** (1935), 807–812, 823–828, 844–849. See sec. 2.

[29] For a discussion on how phases may in principle be determined, see H. Margenau, *Philos. of Sci.*, **30** (1963), 138–157, sec. 10.

[30] *Naturwissenschaften*, **17** (1929), 486–489.

[31] *SH*, p. 21.

apprehending the whole.[32] Our awareness of the particulars is subsidiary, and sometimes may even be subconscious. However, the particulars can never be suppressed altogether, for then the whole would disappear. What is true for perception is also true for concepts. The wavelike *Gestalt* of an atom is a whole whose organized particulars form the above-mentioned structure. Remarks purporting to discuss pure form or pure shape are properly speaking elliptical, in the literary sense. The necessary existence of particulars—*parts*, in fact—is taken for granted and over-looked in speech or writing.[33]

A complementary ellipsis occurs in the usual description of a mechanical system composed of particulars. In this case, the organization of the particulars into a *Gestalt* is obvious and not often mentioned. But without a recognition of this form in itself, adequate explanation of the system is impossible.[34] Because of this, we can agree with Schrödinger on the importance of *Gestalt* ideas, but we may neither use them to do away with the particles, nor make them the sole basis for a fundamental differentiation between wave and particle theories.

3. MATTER WAVES VERSUS ψ-WAVES

One of the criticisms Max Born[35] made of Schrödinger's article "Are There Quantum Jumps?"[36] was that Schrödinger confused de Broglie matter waves in 3-space with ψ-waves in $3n$-space.

To see the difference in physical meaning between the two kinds of waves, let us consider how a beam of electrons in field-free space might be described. The usual wave function ψ for one free electron moving in the $+x$ direction is

$$\psi = c \exp [2\pi i (kx - \nu t)], \qquad (40)$$

[32] See, for example, M. Polanyi, *Personal Knowledge*, pp. 55–58; see also W. T. Scott, "Polanyi's Theory of Personal Knowledge: A Gestalt Philosophy," *Mass. Review*, **3** (1962), pp. 349–368.

[33] In a 1952 lecture Schrödinger remarked again on the *Gestalt* character of the continued identity of a wave form, but avoided the claim that he was speaking of "pure shape," "Unsere Vorstellung von der Materie" in *L'homme devant la Science* (Proceedings of the Rencontres Internationales de Genève, 1952 [Neuchâtel: Éditions de Baconniere, 1952]), pp. 37–54; *WN*, pp. 102–120; trans. and reprinted as "Our Conception of Matter," *WIL*, pp. 161–177. See esp. sec. 7, pp. 175–176.

[34] M. Polanyi, *op. cit.*, pp. 328–331; also M. Polanyi, *The Study of Man* (Chicago: University of Chicago Press, 1959), pp. 44–48.

[35] See pp. 97–99 of ref. 26 above.

[36] *WIL*, pp. 132–160.

where k is the wave number, identified by the de Broglie relation (8) with the momentum p:

$$p = hk = h/\lambda, \qquad (41)$$

and ν is the frequency, given by $\nu = E/h = p^2/2mh$. The constant c may be chosen so that (in the usual interpretation) $\psi^*\psi \, dx$ represents the probability of finding an electron in dx. The probability interpretation implies that many repetitions of the occurrence of an electron in the given state are observed and that $\psi^*\psi$ is proportional to the relative frequency of the given observation. A similar but not logically equivalent interpretation is that many electrons are simultaneously but separately observed in the given state, again yielding a frequency. It is the latter interpretation that appears to refer to a beam.

However, if ψ referred to a beam, the ordinarily negligible interactions between electrons could not be brought in as weak perturbations. They are fundamentally excluded by the fact that eq. (40) only contains the coordinates of one electron. The proper treatment of a beam of electrons by use of ψ-waves is to introduce a ψ that is a function of all the coordinates of all the n electrons in the beam, i.e., a ψ in $3n$-dimensional space.

To treat a beam of electrons instead as a beam of matter waves, one uses the method of second or field quantization mentioned in the previous section. In this method, ψ refers to 3-dimensional space, but becomes an operator (or q-number in Dirac's terminology), that is, a quantum-mechanical variable subject to the uncertainty principle and the whole related set of rules of non-commutative mathematics. Waves described in this way have observable phases, carry energy and momentum, may materialize as particles under low-intensity conditions, and so forth. The fact that in the limit of no interaction the wave length and frequency is the same for these waves as for the ψ-wave for a single electron is the source of their frequent confusion.

These "second-quantized" matter waves form an exact analogue to the electromagnetic field in quantum-mechanical terms. The theoretical apparatus of quantum electrodynamics that correctly describes interference and diffraction of light, as well as the photoelectric and other photon effects, employs the same methods as those used for electron matter-waves.

What, then, of Schrödinger's treatment of the two types of waves? According to Born, Schrödinger wrote in a way that would mislead the nonexpert into believing that the waves of which he spoke were three-dimensional.[37] Heisenberg claimed he actually overlooked the difference.[38] But did he, in fact?

Schrödinger's first use of matter waves actually occurred before the development of wave mechanics. In his article on the Einstein gas theory, discussed in Chapter II (p. 25),[39] he used the concept of occupation numbers for the different modes of vibration and correctly identified the method as an extension of the de Broglie idea. Reference is made to this way of treating a gas in a 1952 lecture,[40] but in this latter instance he did not specify the type of wave he was using, a case in which Born's criticism is merited. Nevertheless, it is clear that from the time of his second paper on wave mechanics[41] Schrödinger was fully aware that waves were $3n$-dimensional.[42] In his 1950 article on elementary particles[43] he explicitly discussed the two different types of wave picture.

However, in "Are There Quantum Jumps?" Schrödinger did not make the distinction explicit and actually referred to both types of waves. In sections 2 and 3 of this article, he referred to "proper modes" without discussing their dimensionality. In section 4, on the Franck–Hertz experiment, he spoke of the electron beam in terms of de Broglie waves. In section 5, on chemistry, the wave picture he used appears to be a $3n$-dimensional one. In sections 6 and 8 on collisions, his reference to products of wave functions (as approximations) makes clear the use of the higher-dimensional space, and in section 11 on single particles he was quite explicit about it. However, the rather obscure discussion of the number of atoms in a body of gas, in section 10, resembles the use of occupation numbers in field quantization, and the last paragraph of the article deals quite clearly with the diffraction of material waves.

In the article "Our Conception of Matter,"[44] he largely focused on the

---

[37] See pp. 99 of ref. 26 above.

[38] "The Development of the Interpretation of the Quantum Theory," in *Niels Bohr and the Development of Physics*, W. Pauli, ed. (New York: McGraw-Hill and London: Pergamon Press, 1955), p. 24.

[39] *Physik. Z.*, **27** (1926), 95–101. This article contains the first discussion of the quantization of translational motion for a particle in a box.

[40] "Our Conception of Matter," *WIL*, p. 176; *WN*, p. 119.

[41] *Ann. Physik*, **79** (1926), 489–527.

[42] See especially *Ann. Physik*, **81** (1926), 109–139, *Phys. Rev.*, **28** (1926), 1049–1070, and *S. B. Preuss. Akad. Wiss.* (1930), 296–303; also the papers on measurement theory cited in ref. 86 below.

[43] "What is an Elementary Particle?" sec. 6, *STM*, p. 206; *WN*, p. 131.

[44] See ref. 33 above.

de Broglie wave idea. He even referred in section 5 to water waves "in two (instead of three) dimensions." However, his discussion of wave normals and trajectories was taken from his second paper on wave mechanics and, to anyone who knows that paper, implies a $3n$-space type of wave picture. He did in this instance refer to the wave length as being automatically a measure of atomic dimensions. This might appear to indicate a 3-dimensional reference, but the fact may be readily derived from my discussion on p. 55 that, with correction for the use of a non-Euclidean metric, the wave length in this space has essentially the same magnitude as it would for a 3-space representation.

There are two points in favor of Schrödinger's position. In the first place, the close logical and physical equivalence of the two types of wave picture has been established. Furthermore, Schrödinger himself considered the method of second quantization to be a fundamental improvement over the other, with respect to its precision and to its treatment of particle statistics.[45] What then is wrong with the inter-changeable use of both types of waves in an article or lecture addressed to people who do not know the formalism of quantum mechanics? The criticisms of Born and Heisenberg seem unduly harsh.

The second point has to do with the problem of what constitutes a clear (*anschaulich*) picture. Schrödinger possessed both the ability to see to the center of a physical problem and an extraordinary facility for clear, witty, and comprehensible popular lectures. Unfortunately, these two talents do not always complement each other, a difficulty which holds for the question of wave pictures. To Schrödinger, the concept of a wave process in hyperdimensional space was quite clear and satisfying. When he tried to present it to an audience, he used three-dimensional analogies. In communicating his main point clearly enough, he saw no need to bridge the gap between two pictures, a gap that was incidental to his main purpose.

4. PARTICLES

Max Born accused Schrödinger of not believing in the existence of particles and, in fact, felt impelled to restate the case for atomism. It should be clear from the above discussion that such structure as does exist in the wave systems has an atomic or particulate nature. But was Schrödinger's belief in particles limited to this fact? Quite the contrary.

[45] "What is an Elementary Particle?" sec. 6, *STM*, p. 206; *WN*, p. 131.

Schrödinger never betrayed the heritage of Boltzmann and Exner. But he challenged the concept of particle *individuality*—quite appropriately, considering what quantum mechanics has to say about it, regardless of interpretation. Let us see what Schrödinger himself said on this subject.

Over and over again[46] Schrödinger emphasized "the enormous significance of this discreteness or *countability* of all that is and happens."[47] His work on the Einstein–Bose gas[48] centered on questions of enumeration. The first paper on wave mechanics introduced quantum numbers in a natural way as the number of nodes or zeros for each particular mode.[49] This type of enumeration of vibration modes was extended into a general concept which in spite of Born's criticism actually was used by Schrödinger to describe atomism, rather than deny it. Planck is usually called the first quantum physicist because he introduced the quantum of energy. Yet if we take Einstein's mass-energy relation seriously, quanta of energy become quanta of mass, and vice versa.[50] Hence Democritus and Leucippus, the inventors of the concept of the atom, were really the first quantum physicists.[51] "Atomism in its latest form is called quantum mechanics," Schrödinger declared in the first sentence of "What is an Elementary Particle?"[52]

The concept of particle has several components which may or may not be made explicit when the concept is used. Countability is certainly basic. The possession of quantitative properties such as mass and charge (and for atomic particles, spin, lifetime, and other still more esoteric properties) is also basic, and has carried over with little change from classical to modern physics. The properties of possessing velocity, momentum, and energy are limited in quantum theory by the uncertainty principle. Wave length and frequency are nonclassical properties that have been added to the sum total of ideas embodied in the word "particle." Last, but far from least, is the concept of the maintenance of

[46] For example, in *NG*, Ch. 7; *WIL*, pp. 103–109; in "The Spirit of Science," *Eranos-Jahrbücher*, **14** (1946), reprinted in *WIL*, pp. 229–250 (sec. 4, pp. 238–243); and, of course, in *Statistical Thermodynamics*.

[47] "Our Conception of Matter," *WIL*, p. 162; *WN*, p. 103.

[48] See ref. 39 above.

[49] Schrödinger later described his motive in inventing wave mechanics as that of "doing away with the point electron," *Elektrische Nachrichten-Technik*, **5** (1928), 485–488.

[50] "Our Conception of Matter," *WIL*, p. 169; *WN*, p. 110.

[51] *SH*, pp. 54–55, *Statistical Thermodynamics*, p. 43, and "2400 Jahre Quanten-mechanik," *Ann. Physik* (6) **3** (1948), 43–48.

[52] *STM*, p. 193; *WN*, p. 121.

identity, which has been lost in the transition from classical to quantum physics.

Schrödinger never denied countability and the invariant properties of particles. Rather he emphasized the wavelike features over the particle-motion features, in particular the lack of identity, as these features seemed to him a crucial matter for the interpretation of the whole theory. In quantum physics, two electrons or two photons are not distinguishable in any way from each other (if abstracted from the possibly different states they are in). Their identity goes even further, however. For instance, when counting states in statistical mechanics, to say that electron A is in state 1 and electron B in state 2, and then repeat the sentence with the letters A and B interchanged is not to describe two possible arrangements but only one.[53] An analogy would be to try exchanging two exactly equal bank balances between the two individuals to whom they are credited.

It is this basic identity that led Schrödinger to describe electrons or atoms as occupied states of a complex system.[54] The numbers of atoms are occupation numbers, closely related to the original node numbers in the wave mechanics of the hydrogen atom. He pointed out quite rightly that in nearly all cases we cannot tell from one moment to the next whether we are following a single given particle. The uncertainty principle itself can be seen to prevent this type of "following" of a particle.[55]

In his article on elementary particles Schrödinger described the conditions under which particles "materialize" and become visible as tracks in a cloud chamber or audible as clicks from a Geiger counter. The essence of the argument for materialization is this. Although electrons do not have individuality, the states they may occupy do (the latter are what quantum numbers enumerate). States may be ordered in terms of contiguity in space. When a series of contiguous states are occupied one at a time, and others nearby are not simultaneously occupied, we have the case of a particle track or trajectory. The track may become visible if the occupation of certain of the states is followed by the development of a droplet or bubble. A track can only be identified if the region is not too crowded, i.e., if only a few adjacent states are occupied.[56]

---

[53] Schrödinger's example from daily life of the counting problem in statistical mechanics is described in Ch. II above, p. 26.

[54] See both the 1950 article and sec. 6 of the 1952 speech, refs. 17 and 33 above.

[55] Another place in which Schrödinger speaks of a particle as a series of events is in *SH*, p. 27.

[56] "What is an Elementary Particle?" *STM*, p. 220; *WN*, p. 140.

A measure for the lack of crowding is that the separation between particles, say of order l, be such that $pl \gg h$, where p is the particle's momentum. In fact, the lateral uncertainty of momentum, Δp_{lat}, must obey $l\,\Delta p_{lat} \gtrsim h$; for a well defined track we must also have $p \gg \Delta p_{lat}$, from which the above result follows.

In this way, the occurrence of particle discreteness is described without implying a sudden appearance of actual individuality. The succession of states in atoms through which a fast charged particle passes would have to be described in ordinary quantum mechanics by means of a large number of coordinates, i.e., in a many-dimensional space. The spreading of a wave from a scattering center through a collection of atoms that could make a track become visible would involve a continued process of materialization related to the collapse or change of wave packet discussed in connection with the theory of measurement (see below, sec. 6). We will have to discuss the probability aspect before we can finish treating this problem of materialization.

Finally, two other comments Schrödinger offered on the subject of particles are relevant. In a review article on the Dirac electron theory,[57] he said that a proper theory of the electron must ultimately be the basis of all physics. If here he meant a proper theory of the quantum mechanics of elementary particles, atomic systems, and radiation, the statement makes sense. But taken literally, it sounds like a reversion to classical particle theory which completely ignores the *Gestalt* aspect of matter.

The other statement was made much later, in a series of Dublin lectures in 1950.[58] Here Schrödinger referred to atomism as a "counterspell of old standing" to dispel the mysterious difficulties of the continuum. He stressed again the centrality of atomism in modern science, in spite of the crisis that the loss of individuality has brought about.

5. COMPLEMENTARITY

We have shown that Schrödinger espoused the concept of atomism that includes electrons, protons, mesons, etc., and nevertheless stressed their wave aspects. Did he use Bohr's concept of complementarity to describe this duality?

---

[57] *Ann. Inst. H. Poincaré*, **2** (1932), 269–310.
[58] *SH*, pp. 53–58.

Bohr's first publication of the idea of complementarity was the report of a speech at Como, Italy, in 1927.[59] The main idea is that space-time and causal descriptions, so woven together in classical physics, have become separated in quantum physics. They cannot both be used at the same time. For instance, a space-time description might involve the motion of a wave packet in time. A wave packet, however, cannot have definite energy and momentum, and so the laws of conservation (which is what Bohr here means by "causality") are not valid exactly. On the other hand, a transition involving an exact energy change cannot be followed in space and time. The two approaches are not *contradictory*, they are *complementary*.

Another expression of this complementarity is the relation between the Schrödinger wave description and the matrix-theory description referring to transitions. Still another form is the relation between the observation or specification of two conjugate variables, such as energy and time or position and momentum, as expressed by the uncertainty principle.[60]

This principle of complementarity has formed the backbone of the so-called Copenhagen interpretation of quantum mechanics.[61] It is clear that Schrödinger does not follow this school in allowing quantum jumps to be treated as complementary to the continuous changes in time discussed earlier. However, there are several ways in which the spirit of complementarity enters his writing.

In the first place, we must emphasize that for Schrödinger, the particles *are* the waves.[62] The wave does not "contain" or "guide" a separate thing that may be conceived of as a particle. Nor does it give the probability that an already existing particle shall appear at a given place. In this view, Schrödinger was perfectly correct. Quantum mechanics does not describe particles as separate from waves in any of these ways. It is true that de Broglie did think this way, and that Einstein proposed that electromagnetic waves were a "ghost field" (*Gespensterfeld*) that guided particles called photons.[63] But this idea does not belong in

[59] N. Bohr, *Nature*, **121** (1928), 580–590; German version in *Naturwissenschaften*, **16** (1928), 245–257.

[60] A clear and extensive description of the idea of complementarity is given by D. Bohm, *Quantum Theory*, Ch. 8.

[61] A recent expression of this interpretation is given by W. Heisenberg, *Physics and Philosophy* (New York: Harper and Row, 1958), Chs. III and VIII.

[62] E. Schrödinger, *Physik. Z.*, **27** (1926), 95–101; *WIL*, pp. 242–243.

[63] Quoted by M. Born, *Z. Physik*, **38** (1926), 804.

modern quantum theory. Insofar as an unconscious residue of it is to be detected in interpretative writing, Schrödinger was correct in attacking it.

This union of particle and wave is part of a more general revolution in physics: the abandonment of the old distinction between particle and field, or particle and force.[64] This change came about in classical physics when relativity disposed of the aether as a medium for the transmission of force, so that fields came to have an equal status in reality with particles, and, furthermore, particles came to be considered as singularities of the fields. It reached its completion with quantum electrodynamics and its various partially successful extensions into meson theory that look upon a given kind of particle as a quantum of a field that acts on another kind of particle.

Where does complementarity appear in this unified picture? One way to see it is to consider that wavelike behavior at its clearest involves a single wave length and frequency, and therefore an infinitely long wave train showing no change in time. Particlelike behavior appears at its best for extremely narrow wave packets that have locations and trajectories. Neither behavior appears often in the extreme case, without a modicum of the other. It will be recognized that this fact is just an expression of the uncertainty principle for position and momentum.

$$\Delta p \, \Delta x \gtrsim h \tag{42}$$

or

$$\Delta(1/\lambda) \, \Delta x \gtrsim 1. \tag{43}$$

Schrödinger used this sort of complementarity throughout his work. We have referred earlier to his use of wave packets (pp. 55–57). A particular example that is relevant to the question of interpretation is his treatment of collisions in "Are There Quantum Jumps?"[65] He pointed out that if we deal with states of exact energy for collision, we must use steady beams, and no "collision" in the ordinary temporal sense of that word occurs. Now such steady-state procedures are normally used for collision problems and have been successful in an enormous variety of cases. Time-varying collisions, in which systems are conceived as approaching, interacting, and receding, are described by wave packets made from the steady-state wave functions of the usual treatment.[66]

[64] *WIL*, pp. 173–175 and *NG*, Ch. I (*WIL*, p. 99).

[65] *WIL*, pp. 150–153.

[66] See, for instance, E. Merzbacher, *Quantum Mechanics* (New York: John Wiley, 1961), Ch. 12, secs. 2 and 3. A general treatment of scattering theory using wave packets is given by T. Sasakawa, *Prog. Theor. Phys.*, **22** (1959), Supp. 11, 69–116.

Schrödinger was disturbed that problems of the wave head or wave front that arrives before the steady state sets in cannot be properly handled by quantum mechanics. He referred to the early work of Sommerfeld on such problems for classical electromagnetic waves entering a dielectric.[67] This is the problem of causality, in the sense of actions not occurring before the arrival of a signal, that is of very considerable use in the modern dispersion theory of particle scattering and interaction.[68] It is interesting that none of the authors dealing with this modern application seems to refer to the older, nonquantum work.

Two further expressions of complementarity, both more elegant and profound, were offered by Schrödinger: that of the longitudinal versus lateral connections of waves and that of localizability versus observability. The former distinction is the following:[69] In a general wave motion in any number of dimensions, propagation occurs along wave normals, at least when the curvature of the wave fronts is not too large. Such propagation may be called the "longitudinal connection" and represents a particlelike trajectory (see pp. 53–56). On the other hand, it is the lateral or transverse connection that is responsible for interference and diffraction, becoming most obvious when the wave fronts are highly curved with radii comparable to the wave length. This is the behavior we recognize as especially wavelike. Each type only becomes noticeable when the other is not; thus we have complementarity.

In 1929 Schrödinger expressed the idea of complementarity in another way,[70] noting that the construct "wave" gives us a mental picture of localizability, but that the wave itself is never observed. On the other hand, observation of a single atomic entity is always observation of a particle (track or counter click, etc.). So observability and localizability are not the same. In contrast to their intimate relation in classical physics, they are now indeed complementary.

[67] A. Sommerfeld, *Physik. Z.*, **8** (1907), 841–842 and *Ann. Physik*, **44** (1914), 177–202. See also L. Brillouin, *Compt. Rend.*, **157** (1913), 914–916, and *Ann. Physik*, **44** (1914) 203–240. For later work, see H. Baerwald, *Ann. Physik*, **6** (1930), 295–369, **7** (1930), 731–760, and **8** (1931), 565–614; F. Borgnis, *Z. Physik*, **117** (1941), 642–650.

[68] The earliest references are R. Kronig, *J. Opt. Soc. Am.*, **12** (1926), 547–558 and *Physica*, **12** (1946), 543–544; W. Schutzer and J. Tiomno, *Phys. Rev.*, **83** (1951), 249–251. Other references with several literature citations are J. S. Toll, *Phys. Rev.*, **104** (1956), 1760–1770, and A. Klein and C. Zemach, *Annals of Phys.*, **7** (1959), 365.

[69] "The Fundamental Idea of Wave Mechanics," Nobel Address; reprinted in *STM*, pp. 166–192, and *WN*, pp. 86–101. See also *WIL*, pp. 174–175.

[70] *Elektrische Nachrichten-Technik*, **5** (1928), 485–488.

A deeper concept of complementarity may also be found in Schrödinger's writings, although he himself never made it explicit. In reference to superposition of states, in accordance with eq. (37), he attacked the idea that a system is always *in* a given energy state, even if we do not know which one. His criticism is sound, for by the general transformation formalism of quantum mechanics, we can rewrite the sum in eq. (37) as a sum over an entirely different set of states that are the eigenfunctions of any other Hermitian operator. It would be just as valid to say that the system is in one of *those* states. What quantum mechanics does tell us is that if we make a precise measurement of energy, we will find the system to "be" in one of the energy eigenstates, whereas if we make a precise measurement of the physical quantity represented by the Hermitian operator of the second expansion, the system will turn out to "be" in one of its states. This process is exactly what Margenau calls the phenomenon of "latent observables."[71] It accounts for the appearance of particlelike behavior in observations when one cannot say the particle was "there" beforehand.

On the other hand, the description of the occupation of states by particles given in the previous section ascribes a very considerable definiteness to a state. If a track is described as a series of occupations of contiguous states, these states are clearly being taken as definite. We have again two complementary descriptions, latent observables and definite states. Since they are useful respectively, for instance, for the continuous observation of radiation from a hot gas and for the observation of a track in a nuclear emulsion, they form a pair not unlike the wave-particle complementarity mentioned earlier.

In certain of his writings, Schrödinger described present-day atomic theory in terms that more closely resemble Bohr's complementarity—for example, in his 1929 speech to engineers,[72] in *Science and Humanism*,[73] and in "Our Conception of Matter."[74] But by and large he did not share the central views of Bohr that I have described above. More precisely, he did not accept complementarity as a fundamental mold into which to fit the ideas of quantum mechanics, but used it only as far as he found it relevant, which was not so far as Bohr.

[71] H. Margenau, *The Nature of Physical Reality* (New York: McGraw-Hill, 1950), p. 175.
[72] See ref. 70 above.
[73] *SH*, pp. 39–47.
[74] *WIL*, pp. 165–168; *WN*, pp. 106–110. A hint at complementarity is given by Schrödinger in "Die Wandlung des physikalischen Weltbegriffs," *WN*, pp. 18–26.

6. QUANTUM THEORY OF MEASUREMENT

The principal relevance of the statistical interpretation of quantum mechanics lies in its application to measurements. Waves may readily be conceived to propagate continuously, but whenever low amplitudes are used with counters of the discrete or particle type, the measurements clearly show a discontinuous type of behavior that is related to the waves in a statistical way. On various occasions Schrödinger had a good deal to say about measurements, and the examination of what he had to say on these occasions will bring to light many of his underlying attitudes and beliefs.

It will be useful to examine one of Schrödinger's last writings as a means of throwing light on his earliest work in this area. In 1955, writing on the philosophy of experiment,[75] he pointed out that astronomy, the great historical model of measurement, was used by the philosophers of science to exemplify experimental method, but that it is not, in fact, an adequate model for most work in physics. The astronomical model involves observations on the planets at a given epoch, prediction of their later positions by using the known (or postulated) laws of motion and of gravitation, and then verifying the prediction by a later observation. The development in time of a system in a given state is the object of interest.

In contrast, measurements in atomic and nuclear physics almost never involve a development in time, but rather are steady-state observations, e.g., of radiation from a given system, or of a steadily scattered beam of particles. Furthermore, it is not a particular state of the system that is of interest, but the nature of the system. Specifically, more information about the Hamiltonian, including transition matrix elements for perturbing potentials, is what is usually sought. Actually, most objects being studied are placed once in an apparatus and either consumed or thrown away before any "happenings" can be studied.[76]

In spite of this situation, Heisenberg discussed the Copenhagen interpretation entirely in terms of successive observations in time.[77] Of course, the interpretive questions are acute in these terms, but no indication is given to the general reader that this is not the usual case.

[75] *Nuovo Cimento*, **1** (1955), 5–15.

[76] Even for the cases to which time-dependent perturbation theory applies, the results are usually phrased in terms of transition rates and applied to steady observations.

[77] *Physics and Philosophy*, Chs. III and VIII.

Margenau's analysis[78] put the matter properly: the connection of one set of observations with another by means of concepts and theories is basically logical; only on occasion is it also chronological.

In the early development of wave mechanics, the main sets of experimental data that called for explanation were spectroscopic results, relating to energy eigenstates. As indicated in section 2, Schrödinger's introduction of the expression $-e\psi\psi^*$ for charge density allowed the treatment in continuous fashion of the radiation that was observed in emission and absorption spectra.

It was nevertheless clear that quantum mechanics should explain counting and collision events as well. Max Born proposed the statistical interpretation, following a suggestion of Einstein's,[79] in order to unite the various aspects of the theory that had so far been developed. It is important to note that Born dealt very little with happenings in time, but largely considered steady-beam types of collision experiments. In his first article, he did not use $\psi^*\psi \, d\tau$ as a probability for a position measurement at all, but used the product $c_n^*c_n$ (see eq. 37, p. 72) to indicate the probability of observing the nth state. Only in the second paper did the usual $\psi^*\psi \, d\tau$ enter, and then only verbally.

As indicated in the last section, wave packets can be used for scattering theory to give time-dependent happenings. The results for comparison with experiment are, however, the same as for the steady-state theory. It is in the conceptual problem of thinking out the relation of continuous waves and discrete counting that time-dependent processes, following in essence the astronomical model, are used in nearly all writing on the quantum theory of measurement. Probably because such writing is thereby removed from the practical situation of experiments as they are actually conceived and carried out, there is an extensive history of disagreement among writers on measurement.

Von Neumann was perhaps the first writer to discuss measurement theory in a logical and systematic way.[80] Although this beginning was made in 1930, most of the writings listed by Margenau in a recent article on measurement [81]date from after 1950. Margenau himself wrote on this

---

[78] *Op. cit.*, Ch. 6.

[79] M. Born, *Z. Physik*, **38** (1926), 803–827, and **40** (1926/7), 167–192. His reference is probably to A. Einstein, *S. B. Preuss. Akad. Wiss.* (1925), 3–14.

[80] J. von Neumann, *Mathematical Foundations of Quantum Mechanics*, trans. R. T. Beyer (Princeton: Princeton University Press, 1953), Ch. III.

[81] "Measurements in Quantum Mechanics," *Annals of Phys.*, **23** (1963), 469–485.

topic in 1936 and 1937,[82] Kemble in 1937,[83] and London and Bauer in 1939.[84] In 1935 and 1936, in response to a paradox-posing article by Einstein, Podolsky, and Rosen,[85] Schrödinger published three articles[86] that contain some important and still-useful material that has been repeated in Margenau's article of 1963. Since the crux of the statistical issue appears in these discussions, let us briefly summarize them here.

The first point is a definition of measurement which I believe to be mistaken. Schrödinger asked: If we make a measurement of a given variable at a given time, what is this a measurement of? Clearly it is not a measure of a preexisting value, since the probability interpretation (which Schrödinger used here without criticism) indicates that different values will be obtained on different occasions. He then maintained that what one measures will be found if the measurement is immediately repeated.[87] However, measurements are often made in such a way that the object detected is destroyed or at least removed from the scene—as when a photon is absorbed in a photocell, or an electron blackens a photographic-emulsion grain. Furthermore, a measurement may involve a finite slit or other experimental source of "error," and the expectation for immediate repetition fails to be exact. Hence this view of measurement should not be a requirement, although it may sometimes be fulfilled.[88]

Nevertheless, let us accept Schrödinger's description for the moment and consider the consequences. Before a measurement is made, for instance of the angle at which a scattered particle is received in a counter, the wave function ψ represents an outgoing spherical wave the amplitude of which is a continuous function over a wide range of angles. After the counter makes a click, the function becomes a very narrowly concentrated one, representing a certainty that a second counter will find the particle

[82] *Phys. Rev.*, **49** (1936), 240–242; *Phil. Sci.*, **4** (1937), 337–370.

[83] E. C. Kemble, *Fundamental Principles of Quantum Mechanics* (New York: McGraw-Hill, 1937), Ch. IX.

[84] F. London and E. Bauer, *La Théorie de l'Observation en Mécanique Quantique* (Paris: Hermann et Cie, 1939).

[85] A. Einstein, B. Podolsky, and N. Rosen, *Phys. Rev.*, **47** (1935), 777–780.

[86] *Proc. Camb. Phil. Soc.*, **31** (1935), 555–563 and **32** (1936), 446–452; *Naturwissenschaften*, **23** (1935), 807–812, 823–828, 844–849.

[87] *Naturwissenschaften*, **23** (1935), 824; Cf. H. Margenau, *The Nature of Physical Reality*, pp. 369–375.

[88] A clue to Schrödinger's insistence on this idea is to be found in *Naturwissenschaften*, **22** (1934), 518–520, where he speaks of some types of observation that do not require any exchange of energy, e.g., the passage of a particle through a slit or an elastic recoilless deflection.

just behind the one that had just detected it. The wave function has "collapsed" in a discontinuous way. The change is usually described by use of von Neumann's "projection postulate," which Margenau rejects.[89]

Schrödinger accepted the collapse of the wave function as inevitable within the frame of reference of its assumptions—especially the assumption that the wave function considered is that of the particle only. We have then the peculiar situation that natural law provides a continuous variation of ψ with time, but that observation by human beings results in a discontinuous, unpredictable change. However, the measuring apparatus clearly also follows natural law, which was not suspended while the particle was passing through the counter. Something is wrong. If we try to maintain the discontinuous collapse of the wave, we find ourselves making ψ a matter of human information and thus subjective, rather than in any sense real. The question of what is real is then left open in a very unsatisfactory way.

The difficulty is considerably lightened when the measuring apparatus is included with the system. Schrödinger's work may be explained in terms of a simple model. A particle A is observed by being bombarded by particle B, the "measuring apparatus." On the rebound, the momentum of particle B is itself measured by allowing B to enter a spectrometer that in classical terms would send particles of different momenta into different channels. Each channel has a counter which will make a visible or audible indication when a particle "goes" through it.

In wave-mechanical terms, the wave for particle B spreads into all the channels. Discontinuous behavior occurs when one counter clicks. Now, to discuss the collapse of the wave for B would involve us in the first step of an infinite regress of collapses untangled by the use of auxiliary systems. Hence we shall assume that the counter removes the particle from observability and no wave exists thereafter.

The important fact is that the momentum of particle A, deduced from that of B by suitable conservation equations and knowledge of initial conditions, will be different for each channel that registers. The paradox of Einstein, Podolsky, and Rosen consists at least partly in the fact that an observation of B after A has rebounded and no longer interacts with A, nevertheless has an effect on the momentum (or whatever) of A.

Now, however, we must take into account the proper dimensionality of ψ. According to wave mechanics, it should be a function of the

[89] "Measurements in Quantum Mechanics," ref. 81, p. 476.

coordinates of *both* A and B. The different channels into which ψ divides are channels in AB space. A large amplitude in a certain channel for the coordinates of B is correlated with a large amplitude for the properly corresponding momentum for A. Measurements on B are obviously correlated with those on A. In Schrödinger's language, the two systems have become "entangled" (*verschrankt*).

The aim of all this is to make a measurement on A. There is no discontinuous collapse of the wave for A, but a continuous sorting out of the joint wave function into channels. An act of counting must now involve the joint AB space, which means that we imagine a set of counters for each particle, correlated pairwise into a single set of channels. When a certain counter is registered for B, the corresponding one will register for A, or one of a subset if the measurement chosen for A is not uniquely related to that of B. If we do not look to see which counter for A has gone off, or if we have no actual counter but imagine one, we can make a meaningful prediction.

Schrödinger said that the discontinuous act now occurs at the moment when the observer "sees" which channel is "occupied," rather than at the moment A is interfered with. This type of discontinuity, a step removed from the *direct* act of measuring A, seems less unsatisfying, and certainly reduces our sense that the wave function is subjective.

However, it is quite clear that the statistical interpretation is essential. Schrödinger referred to ψ in general as a "catalog of expectations," and the breaking of the joint wave function into channels as a "conditional disjunction of expectation catalogs." His Cambridge papers deal with this subject in more technical detail, describing how the choice of different measuring programs for B can lead to the possibility (with nonvanishing probability) of finding A in any state we please. He also showed, as did Margenau,[90] that when the combined system is in a pure state, observation on one will "leave" the other in a mixture (incoherent superposition of pure states). Finally, he discussed time variations between successive measurements on either of the interacting systems.

Schrödinger's conclusion that a quantum-mechanical measurement does not refer to a value existing beforehand but to one existing afterward is neither necessary nor particularly relevant to his method of saving the continuity. In fact, he referred to ψ as giving a relational and conditional bridge *between* two measurements—more properly, he should have said,

[90] *Ibid.*, pp. 474–475; H. Margenau, *Phil. Sci.*, **30** (1963), 11–14 and 138–141.

between a preparation of state and a measurement. This statement is too narrow to describe what he himself has done, for his description of the continuity of ψ through and after the measuring interaction actually allows ψ to go beyond the measurement. However, the usual form of the axioms of quantum mechanics actually does give ψ this restricted bridging quality. Expectation values and probabilities are always calculated as of some time t in terms of a state that presumably had an earlier preparation and of a *single* (if compound) observable. They do not specify anything about either simultaneous or successive observations on a system in a given state.[91]

The most important clue to Schrödinger's views in his discussion of measurement is his rejection of the subjective aspect of the wave function. He continued in later writings to insist that the probabilistic and indeterminate aspects of quantum mechanics have nothing to do with the subject-object relationship in human experience, a relationship he explored so avidly in other contexts. In 1947,[92] he expressed the opinion that the conceptual difficulties posed by the uncertainty relation arise out of the incompleteness of our understanding of waves and corpuscles, not out of subjective interference with nature. In *Science and Humanism*[93] he discussed the question in detail, suggesting that our inability to obtain knowledge about a system because of the interference of the measuring apparatus does not itself close the door to a gapless conceptual model from which predictions and calculations of disturbances can be made. In fact, it should be clear from the above that the wave-mechanical picture, *with* the probability interpretation, forms such a model.

On the other hand, Schrödinger seemed to be treating observables as possessed rather than latent, as Margenau would have them.[94] The concept of latent observables seems to this writer to resolve the problem of what a measurement is *of*, and the question of what reality is *there* besides the wave itself.[95]

[91] The common thought experiments purporting to show how observation of a given variable induces an uncertainty with respect to later observations of the canonically conjugate variable fall outside the usual scope of quantum mechanics.

[92] "On the Peculiarity of the Scientific World View," *WIL*, pp. 194–196; *WN*, pp. 46–47. Schrödinger had proposed in 1930 that the wave-particle difficulty was in fact a reflection of the interaction of subject and object, in "Die Wandlung des physikalischen Weltbegriffs," *WN*, p. 26, but did not pursue this view.

[93] Pages 47–53.

[94] See ref. 71 above, p. 87.

[95] In the same connection, Heisenberg refers to tendencies or Aristotelian *potentia* in *Physics and Philosophy*, p. 53.

Schrödinger voiced two main objections to the idea that the interference with measurement emphasized by supporters of the Copenhagen School represents the boundary between subject and object. In the first place, experimental and theoretical physics are so far removed from existential questions of self that they seem irrelevant to these questions. The boundary does not seem to belong in these surroundings. In the second place, the interference is always by means of instruments, other systems than the one being observed, as our example above indicates. The actual role of the observer remains passive,[96] as it has always been since the ancient Greeks started discussing the relation of the thing perceived to the person perceiving it. (see Ch. V, pp. 110–111.)

In his very last journal publication,[97] Schrödinger reiterated the belief that our experiences of self and our experiences of the world are made of the same elements, differently arranged. The arrangement that yields physical concepts is an effort to describe a reality that exists independently of us. A reduction to subjectivity would defeat this effort. Surely here is one of the grounds for his criticism of the Copenhagen School.

The most authoritative statement of the Copenhagen interpretation is that of Heisenberg.[98] It includes the probability interpretation of the wave function and the concept of latency. While Heisenberg emphasized that the interaction of measuring device with system to be observed is by means of physical instruments rather than directly by the observer, it appears that he attributed a considerable degree of subjectivity to the wave function. Part of this attribution arose out of insistence on the collapse of the wave packet accompanying observation.[99] However, the Copenhagen School claims that classical physics is always used to describe measurements, a claim that neither Schrödinger nor anyone else disputes. It would seem clearer to describe measurements by using quantum mechanics up to the point of the disappearance of the measuring particles into classically responding apparatus, rather than stopping at the point of wave-packet collapse. In fact, if we use the proper space for describing the quantum-mechanical interaction, no

---

[96] Margenau agrees that no light whatever is thrown upon the mind-body problem by the quantum theory of measurement. See "Measurements in Quantum Mechanics," ref. 81, pp. 483–484.

[97] *Nuovo Cimento*, **9** (1958), 162–170.

[98] *Physics and Philosophy*, Chs. III and VIII.

[99] *Ibid.*, p. 142.

collapse occurs.[100] Latent observables appear in the proportion given by the probabilities, and that is all.

Another subjective aspect mentioned by Heisenberg occurs in connection with mixtures. A mixture is an assembly of systems prepared in a variety of different states, with the proportions in each given by a set of relative frequencies or probabilities. These probabilities are classical in nature, exactly like those used in classical statistical mechanics, and do not interfere as do quantum-mechanical probability amplitudes.[101] Both Heisenberg and Margenau called the relative frequencies of a mixture "subjective,"[102] although Margenau used the term to refer to the question of which ensemble is under discussion,[103] while Heisenberg appeared to take the term as indeed implying that the subject-object boundary is involved. Heisenberg even went so far as to imply[104] that no probability is involved in a pure case (represented by a single, definite function ψ), which is in obvious contradiction to quantum mechanics.

I shall not pursue Heisenberg's arguments further, but restrict myself to the conclusion that Schrödinger's objections have a valid basis. An adequate theory of measurement should resolve them without conflicting with the valid, essential elements of the Copenhagen view. In 1950[105] Schrödinger very clearly voiced his conviction that we have not yet found a complete and satisfying theory.

7. THE STATISTICAL INTERPRETATION

To understand Schrödinger's views of Born's statistical interpretation of quantum theory, we must follow four different lines of thought. The first involves the meaning to be given to $\psi^*\psi$, which he interpreted as an actual density in his early papers. The second concerns the work of measurement theory just discussed, and the third the question of whether energy is a statistical concept. Finally, we must consider the interrelation

[100] Schrödinger referred to the collapse of the wave as "ridiculous" in a passage in "Are There Quantum Jumps?" (*WIL*, p. 157), although in the same passage he linked his criticism to the peculiar assertion that we "never experiment with just one electron."

[101] A mixture is sometimes called an "incoherent superposition of states."

[102] H. Margenau, *Phil. of Sci.*, **30** (1963), p. 156.

[103] *Phil. of Sci.*, **30** (1963), p. 9. "Subjective" here means that the selection of a subensemble is only made after information has been obtained from an observation. It does not mean that the conception we have of the system under observation is one of a system whose nature depends on our knowledge.

[104] *Physics and Philosophy*, pp. 54 and 139.

[105] *SH*, pp. 39–47.

of quantum statistics and statistical mechanics—the heritage of Boltzmann.

Schrödinger continued to treat $\psi^*\psi$ as representing something real, even when he actually used it as a probability density, and the wave function was never reduced for him to a matter of information. Insofar as there is no other "thing" about which ψ gives information, he is surely right. The question of whether ψ has more reality than a probability amplitude for happenings is for most physicists a matter of tacit rather than articulate knowing.[106] Without explicitly saying so, Schrödinger seemed to believe both in the reality of the $3n$-dimensional ψ waves *and* in the probabilistic significance of ψ. The work on measurement theory certainly made reference to probability and certainly implied the latency interpretation mentioned above. In the 1955 article on experiment,[107] Schrödinger referred to predictions of probability without indication of disagreement with the idea.

With respect to a statistical interpretation of energy, Schrödinger's position is very weak. As I indicated earlier, he found he could use frequency in place of energy in discussing radiation, resonance, and so forth. But is frequency any easier to define or observe than energy on the atomic scale? The frequency with which the nitrogen atom in the ammonia molecule passes through the hydrogen triangle can, in fact, be used for an atomic clock, but most atomic frequencies are beyond measurement, and in no case can anything but a difference frequency be detected. If the energy were statistical in an electron beam of constant frequency, fluctuations in detectors would surely be noticed, unless energy had no observational significance whatsoever (in which case one could not meaningfully say it was statistical).

Schrödinger's last article[108] deals specifically with energy fluctuations. His starting point is an analogy with entropy, which is a meaningful concept for systems with large numbers of particles, but which breaks down when only a few particles are present. Does the same thing happen to energy? Is Exner's point valid here that we cannot argue from regularity in the large to regularity in the small?[109] Schrödinger was prepared to allow "conservation of frequency" as in eq. (36). If energy

---

[106] M. Polanyi, "Tacit Knowing: Its Bearing on Some Problems in Philosophy," *Revs. Modern Phys.*, **34** (1962), 601–616. See also refs. 32 and 34 above.

[107] *Nuovo Cimento*, **1** (1955), 5–15.

[108] *Nuovo Cimento*, **9** (1958), 162–170.

[109] See Ch. II, p. 31.

means $h\nu$, then it is not statistical. If it does not mean $h\nu$, what does it mean?

One of the main points of contention is that in the usual theory one cannot have definite energies if anything is to happen, any change is to occur. The source for this well-known fact lies in the Fourier analysis of time series. It takes a spread of frequencies to represent pulsed occurrences, those in which the amplitude varies in time. The steady state is characterized by one specific exact frequency. Hence one cannot appeal to the fact that all states of interest actually have a breadth in order to make energy any more statistical than frequency. In fact, the conservation of energy is a rule equivalent to the existence of Hamiltonians that do not depend on the time; the relation of energy and time is expressed in the equation

$$H\psi = \frac{ih}{2\pi}\frac{\partial\psi}{\partial t}, \tag{44}$$

which is a general form of the time-dependent equation (27) (p. 60). The definiteness of energy is a conceptual matter,[110] and Schrödinger's relapse into positivism in order to challenge it is very strange.

A reference to statistical mechanics is also involved in his last article, leading us to the fourth line of thought. Schrödinger did not relish the idea of two independent statistical assumptions in physics, the ergodic hypothesis of statistical mechanics, and Born's assumption that we are now discussing.[111] While he did not reiterate this dissatisfaction in his last article,[112] he did criticize the use of quantum jumps in statistical mechanics. Therefore, we must turn to a direct consideration of this question.

There are two types of "jump" that must be distinguished—the transitions asserted to occur during a radiation or scattering process but not directly part of the measuring process and those represented by the collapse of the wave on measurement. Schrödinger's objections are to the former type; his views on the latter were clearly expressed in 1935 and do not seem to have been modified. The distinction between the two appears clearly in my discussion of the finite wave train on p. 74. The existence of the jump at the time the counter clicks is just that which calls

[110] It is so used in Schrödinger's papers on measurement, ref. 86.

[111] E. Schrödinger, *Ann. Physik.*, **83** (1927), 956–968; *WM*, 137–146.

[112] Perhaps this same dissatisfaction is concealed behind his remark in 1935 that the definition of statistical process is that the second law of thermodynamics applies. ("The Law of Chance: The Problem of Causation in Modern Science," *STM*, pp. 41–42).

into doubt the existence of the jump in the act of radiation. The argument against the former type of jump was given above (pp. 91–95). If "being in a given state" is a possessed observable in Margenau's sense, then we must conceive of jumps taking place. But if this property is a latent observable, Schrödinger was correct; there *are* no jumps.

Schrödinger seemed also to object to the more general terms "transition" and "transition probability"[113] on the grounds that timeless, discontinuous changes are involved. However, transition probabilities as calculated refer to rates at which the coefficients c_n of eq. (37) change with time. The important point for Schrödinger is that a system may be in a state that is a superposition of eigenstates, and that an assemblage of systems may be in a mixture.

This is all quite clearly stated in Schrödinger's book on statistical mechanics,[114] particularly in the appendix to the second edition. He proved there that the treatment of systems by means of continuously varying coefficients rather than by jumps leads to the correct partition function and to the thermodynamic consequences that are so well verified by experiment. In this book and elsewhere[115] Schrödinger made a claim that should be examined in this connection. He argued that to describe a statistical assemblage as being *in* a definite energy state is in "glaring contradiction" to quantum mechanics. He pointed out that the size of a cell in quantum statistical mechanics, namely h^f where f is the number of degrees of freedom, is just enough that any cell will be filled by the quantum correlate of the classical image point of the system, as a consequence of the uncertainty principle. Hence the opportunity for distinguishing between the occupancy of one cell and that of a neighboring one is just washed out, so that one can no longer distinguish between state-occupancies in a sharp way. Now, this is surely correct for the p-q phase space to which the cells refer, but if energy were used as a parameter, the washing out of levels would involve not this cell-size assumption but time uncertainty instead. The contradiction does not seem so glaring when viewed this way.

It is nevertheless true that a system with strictly exact energy could never approach equilibrium or change in any way, since nothing could happen. This is a valid reason for insisting on a superposition of states.

[113] "Our Conception of Matter," *WIL*, pp. 173–175; *WN*, pp. 116–117.
[114] *Statistical Thermodynamics*, 2nd ed., p. 5 and Appendix, pp. 89–90.
[115] "Conceptual Models in Physics and Their Philosophical Value," *STM*, pp. 162–163, and ref. 108 above.

However, the most important reason is that in fact we can neither deal with single energy states nor with "pure" (coherent) superpositions. Mixtures must be used if statistical mechanics is to account for the actual situation with fluctuating energies and only approximately constant temperatures.

What can we conclude? First, we can say that Schrödinger really accepted the statistical interpretation. It is implied in his description of materialization and his theory of measurement. However, because of his objection to subjectivity and complementarity in its fullest sense, he spoke against it. He expressed the hope that in some modification of the statistical interpretation there might come a clarification of the conceptually difficult situation in quantum mechanics.

But he often seemed to lose sight of the statistical aspect. For instance, his description of a chemical reaction[116] implies the development of a wave of an enormously large number of channels. The actual observation of a collection of product molecules constitutes the observation of a particular channel, or better, of one of a number of experimentally indistinguishable channels. The probability aspect is clearly implied here, but his description would lead one to believe that no quantum mechanical statistics were involved at all.

Schrödinger was correct on one extreme of his critique—there are no quantum jumps. On the other, he seems wrong—energy is not a statistical quantity.

8. A RETURN TO CLASSICAL PHYSICS?

We are now ready for our original question. Was Born right that Schrödinger sought a return to "the classical physics of clearly comprehensible events"?

Undoubtedly Born was correct. However, it is important to point out that Schrödinger understood certain ways in which quantum mechanics is—and will remain—nonclassical.

Schrödinger clearly understood that the addition of frequencies, as in eqs. (33) or (36), is nonclassical. Two classically vibrating systems would show both the sum and difference of separate frequencies, three systems would show four different combinations, and so on. The quantum result arises from the use of the complex instead of the real form for the periodic time factors in eq. (37). However, as we pointed out above, a complex

[116] "Are There Quantum Jumps?" *WIL*, pp. 143–146.

function ψ can be replaced by a pair of real functions, which would have the same consequences. Whether this behavior is nonclassical or may be treated as an extension of classical ideas is a matter of definition. I have already indicated that the use of waves in $3n$-space is not a sign of nonclassical behavior.

The concept of limited amplitude as indicated by the normalization condition $\int \psi^* \psi \, d\tau = 1$ is far more a nonclassical idea. Superposition of waves is, of course, part of classical physics, but the idea that the amplitude of one mode must decrease as that of another is added seems hard to understand. It is an unusual type of conservation law, which in the transformation of the theory to an occupation-number representation appears more normal as the conservation of the number of particles. Thus here, too, we may find a type of classical behavior, although Schrödinger himself said in 1929 that the wave mechanics of continuous functions was not a return to classical physics,[117] and that the variables of quantum mechanics were related to those of classical physics in name only.[118]

The central nonclassical aspect of quantum mechanics is, of course, that of probability. It is here that clear mental pictures break down, and there is no doubt that Schrödinger wanted to find a clear picture. He thought he had found it in 1926, as we have indicated. In 1928,[119] he described the situation with reference to a hypothetical student who is asked how we can understand the necessity for the large aperture of a highly-resolving telescope when it has been shown by Einstein that light is absorbed in photons, highly localizable at the surface of a photocell. When the student replies, "I do not know," he is rated *summa cum laude* for giving the right answer!

In several writings Schrödinger dealt more specifically with the conceptual problem. In another 1928 lecture[120] he referred to the gaps in the quantum mechanical picture of atomic systems caused by the difficulty of even conceiving of certain events, e.g., trajectory or orbit of a particle. He suggested that the answer to this "desperate situation" might lie in constructing a new model in which the areas represented by the gaps did not even enter. In 1946 he expressed the necessity for the construction of a satisfactory model using both wave and particle prop-

[117] *Naturwissenschaften*, **7** (1929), 486–489.
[118] *Naturwissenschaften*, **23** (1935), 810.
[119] *Elektrische Nachrichten-Technik*, **5** (1928), 485–488.
[120] "Conceptual Models in Physics," *STM*, pp. 148–165.

erties, "difficulties which, despite great partial success, have not yet been solved."[121] As I have pointed out, he expressed the hope in *Science and Humanism* for a gapless model that would allow us conceptually to include the effects of our disturbances. Wave mechanics, he said, is only a temporary makeshift. In his 1952 article on the nature of matter he expressed his optimism for "something better than the mess of formulas that today surrounds our subject."[122] Finally, in his book, *Mind and Matter*,[123] he referred to quantum uncertainty as a possible contamination in our over-all view of the comprehensibility of the world and expressed the hope that a noncomplementary model may someday be found.

Schrödinger said more than once that science primarily has meaning and value in relation to its cultural context.[124] Furthermore, it can only develop by unfolding out of its own history. Did he, in his critique of quantum mechanics, belie these words and remove himself too far from the main body of physics? How did he himself relate to the cultural milieu?

Schrödinger clearly did not follow the apparently popular fashion of positivism, for he focused attention on the model, the concepts, the theory, rather than on the observation. The question is not merely whether we can account for our observations, but, for instance, "whether actually *natura facit saltus* [nature makes a jump] or no."[125] And Schrödinger was right. Finding out what really happens, understanding the nature of things—these have been part of the spirit of science ever since it began. In spite of all the talk of positivism, this heuristic urge permeates the whole of western culture.

As for the body of physics, Schrödinger worked within its conceptual framework. With considerable justification but no great success, he sought to reinterpret quantum mechanics in accord with the soundest insights of physics as he understood them. He was concerned for clarity and comprehensibility, and while he accepted all the calculated results of quantum mechanics, he felt uneasy about the claims made for the necessity of abandoning clear pictures, for the requirement of

[121] "The Spirit of Science," *WIL*, p. 242.
[122] "Our Conception of Matter," *WIL*, p. 162; *WN*, p. 103.
[123] *MM*, Ch. III.
[124] Schrödinger discussed the importance of the cultural milieu in "Are There Quantum Jumps?" *WIL*, pp. 132–136, "Is Science a Fashion of Our Times?" and "Physical Science and the Temper of the Age," *STM*, pp. 81–105 and 106–132.
[125] "Are There Quantum Jumps?" *WIL*, p. 150.

complementarity, and for the finality of the statistical approach. He was not interested in a return to Newtonianism, but because he was a classical physicist at heart, he sought for a picture based on continuity and on statistics of the type inherited from Boltzmann and Exner. Both his philosophical writings and his research efforts showed his continuous search for deeper understanding with a view to clearing the way for new discoveries. His loyalty to Exner and Boltzmann and to his own ideas of wave mechanics was strong, but it did not overcome his deeper loyalty to truth.

Whether or not Schrödinger's hope for an *anschaulich* model proves justified, we can respect the spirit in which he pursued it. His intuition ran deep in many ways. Time may reveal that he was prophetic in his anticipation of a new level of comprehensible reality.

Chapter V

Nature and the Self

ἡμεῖς δέ, τίνες δὲ ἡμεῖς;
And we, who are we, anyway?
PLOTINUS

1. INTRODUCTION

From the days in which physics was called "natural philosophy,"
physicists have sought universal principles to explain the material world.
At the height of classical physics in the nineteenth century, the accepted
principles were based on a view of matter as concrete and picturable—
made of hard, indestructible, measurable atoms. Explanation then
consisted of finding laws of motion for matter, laws which were understood to allow a precise calculation of the succession of states that any
material object or collection of objects would pass through in the course
of time.

At the turn of the century, however, just as physicists were becoming
convinced that all the important laws had already been discovered, the
disturbing evidence for the quantum and relativistic pecularities of
nature began to appear. The resulting transformation of physics was a
development in which Schrödinger himself played a major part. In
place of the old clarity about matter and motion, new experimental
evidence pointed to phenomena on the sub-microscopic scale which are
difficult to describe in theoretical or mathematical terms and which
even seem beyond our intuitive powers to visualize. Contemporary
physicists have reexamined their conception of matter in the hope of
finding a more satisfactory basis for understanding the material world.
They have been led not only to question the very possibility of a causal or
picturable explanation but to reconsider the nature of explanation itself.
It is not surprising that persons with a strong metaphysical curiosity are
attracted to physics or that many such persons go beyond the boundaries
of their discipline to explore deep questions of value and meaning. Many
of the very scientists who have made the most profound discoveries about

matter and its peculiarities—men like Einstein, Bohr, and Heisenberg—are among those who have been most drawn to philosophical questions.

Erwin Schrödinger was one of these. He struggled rigorously and creatively with the problem of finding satisfying mental pictures of atomic behavior. And his inquiry went beyond the puzzles of atomic physics to the even deeper problems of the existence and quality of the world, of the self, and of the intimate connection of the self to the world. In his early years (see Ch. I) Schrödinger hoped to combine lecturing on theoretical physics with the study of philosophy, "being deeply imbued at the time with the writings of Spinoza, Schopenhauer, Mach, Richard Semon, and Richard Avenarius."[1] More than forty years later, writing in Alpbach the summer before his death, Schrödinger looked back on his earlier aspirations and described as the "fulfillment of a very long cherished wish" the publication of the little book which he entitled *My View of the World*. It is worth noting that the writing of the two essays which comprise that volume was separated by a period of thirty-five years. The first was written in 1925, shortly before Schrödinger's appointment as successor to Max Planck in Berlin; the second in 1960, two years after his appointment as Professor Emeritus at the University of Vienna. The underlying unity of Schrödinger's thought is indicated by the fact that the two essays are not only closely related in theme but intertwined with key problems which concerned him in the intervening years.

Schrödinger was a philosopher in the root sense of the word—a lover of wisdom. He described the wellspring of philosophy as the kind of wonder and surprise he himself felt about the nature of things:

> It was said by Epicurus, and he was probably right, that all philosophy takes its origin from θαυμάζειν, philosophical wonder. The man who has never at any time felt consciously struck by the extreme strangeness and oddity of the situation in which we are involved, we know not how, is a man with no affinity for philosophy—and has, by the way, little cause to worry.[2]

Unfortunately, it was not Schrödinger's way to lay out his philosophical ideas in a systematic treatise. Instead he expressed his views in popular articles and lectures designed to convey difficult ideas in non-technical terms with vivid images and simple examples. Most of this work is contained in eight slim volumes, which occupy a scant four inches on a library shelf. The reader will soon discover that there is nothing slight

[1] *MVW*, p. viii.
[2] "Seek for the Road," *MVW*, p. 10.

Nature and the Self

about these books except their size. They are in themselves a testament to one of Schrödinger's overriding interests: the synthesis of the knowledge of specialists with popular thought in language the layman can understand.

Schrödinger's eight nontechnical books are *What is Life?* (1944), an exploration of the physical bases for genetic and cellular processes; *Science and Humanism*; *Physics in Our Time* (1952), the text of four lectures on the spiritual bearing of science on life, on our present conception of matter, and on the problem of indeterminacy; *Nature and the Greeks* (1954), a historical and critical account of the Greek roots of modern science; *Mind and Matter* (1959), a discussion of consciousness, ethics and self-identity; *My View of the World* (1964), two essays contending that there is only one single consciousness of which we are all aspects; and three collections of essays, *Science Theory and Man* (1935 and 1957), the Doubleday paperback edition of *What is Life?* (1957), and *Was ist ein Naturgesetz? Beiträge zum naturwissenschaftlichen Weltbild* (1962).[3]

The motive underlying all the diversity of Schrödinger's work is the search for an answer to the question of Plotinus: "And we, who are we, anyway?"

In Schrödinger's view, knowledge of the self and knowledge of the world are intimately interrelated. Achieving knowledge of the self and knowledge of the spatial and temporal surroundings of one's environment are part of the same quest. In the introductory lecture of *Science and Humanism*, Schrödinger rejects the notion that the primary value of scientific research lies in transforming technology and improving the conditions of human society.

> You may ask...What, then, is in your opinion the value of natural science? I answer: Its scope, aim and value is the same as that of any other branch of human knowledge. Nay, none of them alone, only the union of all of them, has any scope or value at all, and that is simply enough described: it is to obey the command of the Delphic deity, Γνῶθι σεαυτόν, get to know yourself...I am born into an environment—I know not whence I came nor whither I go nor who I am. This is my situation as yours, every single one of you. The fact that everyone always was in the same situation, and always will be, tells me nothing. Our burning question as to the whence and whither —all we can ourselves observe about it is the present environment. That is why we are eager to find out about it as much as we can. That is science,

[3] The last named volume contains German versions of some of the articles in the two previous works, and one essay not found elsewhere.

learning, knowledge, that is the true source of every spiritual endeavour of man. We try to find out as much as we can about the spatial and temporal surroundings of the place in which we find ourselves put by birth. And as we try, we delight in it, we find it extremely interesting.[4]

Actually, in spite of Schrödinger's insistence on the integration of all knowledge, his writings reveal relatively few *formal* points of contact between physics and philosophy. This is not because Schrödinger wished to keep his professional and avocational interests separate—he would have been the last man to wish that—but rather because he found that by and large the conclusions of wave mechanics or of any of the rest of his prodigious scientific output had little to do with his view of the world.[5] Although there are a number of informal and rather subtle ways in which his interest in chance and causality, in the heritage of Boltzmann and Exner, and in the difficulties of quantum theory did enter into his world view, the principal connection is in the person of Schrödinger himself: he wrote his philosophically oriented essays as a practicing theoretical physicist who was deeply concerned with fundamental questions.

All his lifetime Schrödinger struggled with problems of nature and the self. He was concerned not only with how we comprehend the world but with the conviction that the world is, in fact, comprehensible; not only with how the self gets in the way of observing the world, but with the practice of leaving the self out of the objectified world as we conceive it. Schrödinger expressed these concerns in terms of two principles— *comprehensibility* and *objectivation*—features of the scientific world view which form the basis for all scientific inquiry.

In the following pages I will explore in some detail the place of these principles in Schrödinger's work and their importance for contemporary thought. Since I am not a philosopher, the exploration will have certain limitations. I will not, for the most part, attempt to evaluate the sources of Schrödinger's ideas or their place in the history of philosophy. Nor will I try to go beyond his publications or even to deal with all the content of his wide-ranging nontechnical writings, although the development of the themes of comprehensibility and objectivation will provide the opportunity to touch on many facets of his work. In short, my discussion will be that of a working physicist who has pondered some of the same questions that disturbed Schrödinger and who has received

[4] *SH*, pp. 4–5.
[5] *MVW*, pp. vii–viii.

stimulation and insight from his writings. If, despite its limitations, this account encourages others to explore Schrödinger's work for themselves, it will have served its purpose.

2. COMPREHENSIBILITY AND OBJECTIVATION

Schrödinger defined comprehensibility as "the hypothesis that *the display of Nature can be understood*. . . . It is the non-spiritistic, the non-superstitious, the non-magical outlook."[6] While it may be argued that a consistent animistic view also implies a type of comprehensibility, Schrödinger clearly meant by the term the belief that things happen in some type of ordered, picturable process following natural law. Although our methods of comprehending the world and the specific fruits of inquiry have changed tremendously over the years, the belief that comprehension is possible in terms of natural law has been a persistent feature of science from the beginning.

Schrödinger's concern about comprehensibility was obviously stimulated by the struggles over the interpretation of quantum mechanics (see Ch. IV). He turned away from the widely accepted Copenhagen view that matter on the atomic scale is basically incomprehensible. In "Our Conception of Matter" he wrote:

A widely accepted school of thought maintains that an objective picture of reality—in any traditional meaning of that term—cannot exist at all. Only the optimists among us (and I consider myself one of them) look upon this view as a philosophical extravagance born of despair in the face of a grave crisis. We hope that the fluctuations of concepts and opinions only indicate a violent process of transformation which in the end will lead to something better than the mess of formulas that to-day surrounds our subject.[7]

The notion of comprehensibility is not restricted to consideration of the inorganic world. At least some features of living organisms are comprehensible in scientific terms. As we move from the study of the simplest biological organisms to forms of life more and more nearly related to ours, we continue to believe in comprehensibility. But when we go one step further and include the self in the comprehensible world, we confront the problem of *objectivation*, the second of Schrödinger's concerns.

By objectivation Schrödinger meant the practice of removing the knower, the observing self, from the world that is being studied. Nature

[6] *NG*, p. 88. Reprinted in *WIL*, p. 103; *WN*, pp. 102–103.
[7] *WIL*, pp. 161–162; *WN*, pp. 102–103.

is treated as pure object, "out there," removed from those who examine it.[8] *How* we look at nature "out there"—whether we consider it in objectivist fashion to be the only reality or whether we simply try to look at it objectively, free from irrelevant subjective influences—is a question to be discussed quite independently from the principle of objectifying the world in order to examine it. Since the very effort of comprehension is an effort of subject relating to object, the principle of comprehensibility would make no sense if objectivation were not carried out, at least to some extent. However, it is just this subject-object relation which makes comprehension of the self a meaningless or contradictory notion. Only if both the notions of comprehensibility and objectivation are modified in some way, can we hope to speak meaningfully of understanding the self.

Schrödinger believed that deep metaphysical insight is needed to modify these notions successfully and to learn even a little about the mystery of who we are. He considered it not at all surprising that efforts at comprehending the world around us—efforts which no matter how they failed have insisted on comprehensibility as a principle—should function by cutting out of the world picture the mind in which the picture is constructed. Our bodies are in the world we look at; they make us think our minds are in it, but this is an illusion. Because we are not aware that we cut out our minds when we construct our scientific world picture, we are astonished to discover that the result is deficient. Of that picture Schrödinger wrote:

> It gives a lot of factual information, puts all our experience in a magnificently consistent order, but it is ghastly silent about all and sundry that is really near our heart, that really matters to us. It cannot tell us a word about red and blue, bitter and sweet, physical pain and physical delight; it knows nothing of beautiful and ugly, good or bad, God and eternity. Science sometimes pretends to answer questions in these domains, but the answers are very often so silly that we are not inclined to take them seriously.[9]

Schrödinger might have added that objectivation is responsible for much of the depersonalization and denial of values in our civilization. Comprehensibility also has consequences of crucial significance in the contemporary struggle for meaning. The conviction that the world is comprehensible is commonly extended without limit, leading to a widespread belief that science has universal applicability. No place appears to

---

[8] "On the Peculiarity of the Scientific World View," *WIL*, p. 183; *WN*, p. 33.
[9] *NG*, p. 93.

be left for mystery and no area of inquiry is reserved for intuition and faith.[10]

Deeply concerned with the difficulties of a world view founded on scientific belief in comprehensibility and objectivation, Schrödinger developed an interest in the historical origins of these two key notions. It was his thesis that considerable insight into our present situation—both regarding the difficulties of comprehending the quantum nature of matter and of locating the self in our world picture—could be gained by a study of history. In returning to the thought of the early Greeks, he believed "there is not only...the hope of unearthing obliterated wisdom, but also of discovering inveterate error at the source where it is easier to recognize."[11]

In the following sections I will first examine Schrödinger's study of the historical roots of comprehensibility and objectivation. Then I shall turn to an account of what in Schrödinger's view are proper terms for a physical comprehension of the world. The next step is to apply these terms to living systems. In examining life, we face the problem of the relation of mind and matter. Here we are confronted head-on by the nature of objectivation and the subsequent gaps in our knowledge that it has helped to create. The two last sections are devoted to consideration of these consequences of objectivation. A summary of Schrodinger's understanding of the process and an account of the doctrine of identity which he accepted as a solution to the problem will be followed by a critique of his solution.

3. ROOTS IN HISTORY

Schrödinger claimed that the features of comprehensibility and objectivation were built into science at its origin, and are not to be treated primarily as matters of logic or empirical necessity the genesis of which is irrelevant to their validity. On two occasions, quoting others, he expressed his answer to the possible objections of those who see no practical value in the study of ancient thought. The first, translated from Theodor Gomperz's *Griechische Denker*, concludes:

[10] Along with insistence on the universality of science there is the corollary, more widely held than justified, that common methods must be valid in all areas of science, and the further conclusion, with even less justification, that the methods of physics, the most successful science, should be taken as the model for all other sciences. Contention over scientific methods underlies many disagreements about both facts and values in modern life.

[11] *NG*, pp. 16–17.

Nearly our entire intellectual education originates from the Greeks. A thorough knowledge of these origins is the indispensable prerequisite for *freeing* ourselves from their overwhelming influence. To ignore the past is here not merely undesirable, but simply impossible. You need not know of the doctrines and writings of the great masters of antiquity, of Plato and Aristotle, you need never have heard their names, none the less you are under the spell of their authority. Not only has their influence been passed on by those who took over from them in ancient and in modern times; our entire thinking, the logical categories in which it moves, the linguistic patterns it uses (being therefore dominated by them)—all this is in no small degree an artifact and is, in the main, the product of the great thinkers of antiquity. We must, indeed, investigate this process of becoming in all thoroughness, lest we mistake for primitive what is the result of growth and development, and for natural what is actually artificial.[12]

Schrödinger took the second quotation from the preface of John Burnet's *Early Greek Philosophers*:

... it is an adequate description of science to say that it is "thinking about the world in the Greek way." That is why science has never existed except among peoples who came under the influence of Greece.[13]

Schrödinger commented, "This is the most concise justification a scientist could wish for, to excuse his propensity for 'wasting his time' in studies of this kind."[14]

Schrödinger's first writing on the history of science was his article "On the Peculiarity of the Scientific World View," which drew its historical material from John Burnet, Theodor Gomperz, S. Cyril Bailey, Benjamin Farrington, and Hermann Diels. The historical part of this article was considerably amplified and rearranged in *Nature and the Greeks*, based on the 1948 Shearman Lectures at University College, London. The book does not pretend to have anything like the thoroughness and completeness of a work like Sarton's *History of Science*, even in its treatment of the pre-Socratics (Ionians and others) in whom Schrödinger was especially interested. However, *Nature and the Greeks* provides a lively and clear sketch of the principal steps in the development of Greek science.

As one of the roots of the concept of comprehensibility, Schrödinger traces the historical problem of epistemology: the competition between

[12] T. Gomperz, *Griechische Denker* (3rd ed.; Leipzig: Veitl und Comp., 1911), I, p. 419; quoted in *NG*, pp. 17–18; *WIL*, pp. 101–102.

[13] J. Burnet, *Early Greek Philosophy* (4th ed.; London: A. and C. Black, 1930); quoted in *NG*, p. 18; *WIL*, p. 102.

[14] *NG*, p. 18; *WIL*, p. 102.

reason and the senses as the proper means for establishing the nature of the real world. On one side of the conflict was Parmenides (ca. 480 B.C.), who proposed on the basis of "pure reason" that all is one; distinctions, variations, changes are all illusory. In contrast, according to Schrödinger, the great Sophist Protagoras (ca. 440 B.C.) spoke of sense perceptions as the only things which really exist. It was the atomist Democritus (ca. 420 B.C.), considered by Schrödinger to be the most advanced epistemologist of the ancients,[15] who showed that both reason and the senses must be used.

In so doing, Democritus put his finger on the crucial difficulty, the one we still struggle with today. He referred to atoms as having in themselves none of the sensual qualities which are the common everyday experience of mankind and *from which we* (or at least the atomists) *infer the existence of atoms.* Schrödinger quoted a fragment of Democritus taken from Galen as illustration. The Intellect (διάνοια) is engaged in a contest with the Senses (αἰσθήσεις).

> The Intellect: "Ostensibly there is colour, ostensibly sweetness, ostensibly bitterness, actually only atoms and the void."
> The Senses: "Poor intellect, do you hope to defeat us while from us you borrow your evidence? Your victory is your defeat."[16]

In short, in its effort to comprehend the nature of things our reason proposes a world view which fails to account for the sense impressions upon which its conclusions rest.

Schrödinger next considered the Pythagoreans (ca. 532 B.C.), who stressed the role of reason over that of the senses. They not only took the world to be comprehensible but made both a religion and a science out of the conviction that number is the ultimate reality. In spite of much fantasy and arrogant mysticism, the Pythagoreans made more headway toward an understanding of the celestial universe than any other group of ancients, developing, for instance, a heliocentric view of the solar system, with a rotating earth belonging to the family of planets. Schrödinger characterized the Pythagoreans as "the prototype of a school of thinkers with strongly scientific orientation and at the same time with a well-marked bias, bordering on religious prejudice, towards reducing the edifice of nature to pure reason."[17]

[15] *NG*, p. 29.
[16] *Ibid.*, p. 30.
[17] *Ibid.*, p. 32.

Schrödinger turned next to a group of philosophers whom he considered close to the Pythagoreans in their clearly scientific outlook and aims but opposed to them in their reliance on the senses. Included in this group are those belonging to the Milesian or Ionian School—Thales, Anaximander, Anaximenes, Xenophanes, and Heraclitus, and the atomists Leucippus and Democritus—who "take the world as given to us by our senses and try to explain it, not bothering about the precepts of reason any more than the man in the street does, from whose way of thinking theirs is a direct descendant."[18]

According to Schrödinger, the birth of science can be ascribed to the contributions made by the Ionian School during the remarkable sixth century B.C. The Ionians contributed three crucial concepts: the idea that all nature is comprehensible;[19] the conception that all the infinite variety of things is intrinsically made of the same stuff; and the notion that changes like condensation and rarefaction can account for the different forms of the same stuff.

Schrödinger recalled the experience of many a young student who comes upon the ideas of the Ionians in a brief survey of the period. Quite typically the student is bored or amused to read that one philosopher taught that everything is air, another that everything is water, and a third that everything is fire. What great happening in the history of ideas, Schrödinger asked, moves us to "label this event the Birth of Science and to describe Thales of Miletus as the first scientist in the world?" According to Schrödinger, it was the introduction of the idea of comprehensibility:

> The grand idea that informed these men was that the world around them was something *that could be understood*, if one only took the trouble to observe it properly; that it was not the playground of gods and ghosts and spirits who acted on the spur of the moment and more or less arbitrarily, who were moved by passions, by wrath and love and desire for revenge, who vented their hatred, and could be propitiated by pious offerings. These men had freed themselves of superstition, they would have none of all this. They saw the world as a rather complicated mechanism, acting according to eternal innate laws, which they were curious to find out. This is, of course, the fundamental attitude of science up to this day. To us it has become flesh of our flesh, so much so that we have forgotten that somebody had to find it out, make it a programme, and embark on it.[20]

[18] *Ibid.*, p. 51.

[19] G. Sarton, *A History of Science* (Cambridge, Mass.: Harvard University Press, 1952), p. 213.

[20] *NG*, p. 55.

The origin of our modern concept of atoms was in the atomism of Democritus and Leucippus (ca. 450 B.C.). They believed that physical laws of nature determined the behavior of *all* atoms, both those of the inorganic world and those within all living things. Their view was passed on in the writings of Epicurus (ca. 300 B.C.) and Lucretius (99–55 B.C.), to be taken up years later by Gassendi (1592–1655) and supported by Newton (1642–1727). Dalton (1766–1844) reintroduced it into physics and chemistry in essentially our modern form. Interestingly enough, despite the fact that neither Democritus nor Gassendi had any of the wide experimental evidence of modern physics, the crucial features of the ancient theory are still present in the modern one—greatly developed, but basically unchanged.

Democritus' theory, however, included the notion that the soul consists of fine, highly mobile atoms, properly spaced within the body to make it function. Schrödinger termed this idea a "truly absurd feature"[21] of the theory, for it put the operation of the will on a parallel to other functions in a living body and seemed to require that a similar law of necessity should apply. The problem of free will versus determinism was thus raised more than 2400 years ago. The real difficulty, for Schrödinger, is deeper than the problem of making the self into a separately operating mechanism within the body. In his view, the self cannot be found *anywhere* in the comprehensible world, for the very act of considering the world as comprehensible puts it "out there," as an object removed from the self. In short, objectivation inevitably had to grow up as a concomitant of comprehensibility.

4. THE SEARCH FOR THE "WORLD IN COMMON"

In *Nature and the Greeks* Schrödinger discussed the "very deep epistemological insight" of Heraclitus (ca. 500 B.C.) that we can only find a reliable world picture if "this world can be so constructed as to be *in common* to all of us, or rather to all *waking, sane* persons."[22] A person's own sense perceptions must be checked by comparison with the perceptions of others if he is to rely on these perceptions for clues about the real world. Comprehensibility seems then to mean that the display of nature can be understood by men acting in common, that together they can share experiences, conceptions, and the processes of reason to find an explanation of the real world around them. To understand more explicitly what

[21] *Ibid.*, p. 78.
[22] *Ibid.*, p. 70.

113

Schrödinger meant by comprehensibility, let us see what he said about this communal search in present-day science. What is our goal in taking and sharing data and in forming theories from this data? Do we take the observations of others on faith, or verify them all ourselves? Can we develop our shared knowledge dispassionately, free from cultural influences, or must we operate emotionally, in a milieu from which we cannot escape?

According to Machian positivism, the important elements of our world in common are the data themselves. In this view the only proper function of a theory is to provide an economical way of describing past and future observations. Schrödinger discussed this view and rejected it[23] because the bare results of observation do not have explanatory power. He believed that mere knowledge of the data, or even prediction of future data, is not of intrinsic interest to scientists. Only if the observations seem to bear on reality in some way, whether descriptively or quantitatively, do they satisfy a scientist's desire for comprehension.

Schrödinger spoke with considerable feeling on the inadequacies of positivism:

> ...call to mind that sense of misgiving, that cold clutch of dreary emptiness which comes over everybody, I expect, when they first encounter the description given by Kirchhoff and Mach of the task of physics (or of science generally): "a description of the facts, with the maximum of completeness and the maximum economy of thought"; a feeling of emptiness which one cannot master, despite the emphatic and even enthusiastic agreement with which one's theoretical reason can hardly fail to accept this prescription. In actual fact (let us examine ourselves honestly and faithfully), to have *only* this goal before one's eyes would not suffice to keep the work of research going forward in any field whatsoever. A real elimination of metaphysics means taking the soul out of *both* art *and* science, turning them into skeletons incapable of any further development.[24]

What Schrödinger meant by countering positivism with "metaphysics" is that science requires assertions about reality which go beyond any logical consequences derivable from data. He illustrated his use of the term by referring to the meaning of printed words:

---

[23] "On the Peculiarity of the Scientific World View," *WIL*, pp. 190–192, 194–196; *WN*, pp. 40–42, 44–47. See also "Are There Quantum Jumps?" *WIL*, p. 154, and the brief comments at the end of Chapter IV above.

[24] "Seek for the Road," *MVW*, pp. 3–4.

Metaphysics includes, amongst other things—to take just one quite crude example—the unquestioning acceptance of a more-than-physical—that is, transcendental—significance in a large number of thin sheets of wood-pulp covered with black marks such as are now before you.[25]

Schrödinger had several other comments to make about the importance of metaphysics in science, in the course of which he appeared to use the word in several different ways. He suggested, for instance, that hunches leading us on to precise study are metaphysical. While it is true that vague hints often spur us on to research, much as a dim shape looming out of a fog calls out our efforts to see clearly, and that such hints have to be pursued at some length before they can be verified, it seems better to describe them as heuristic clues with a large component of tacit knowledge, as does Polanyi,[26] than to call them metaphysical.

Schrödinger also used "metaphysics" in Kant's "regulative" sense, as a rule of inquiry no longer needed when the results are in, a scaffolding to be taken down. With Kant's rejection of "constitutive" metaphysics, i.e., propositions about the nature of particular things deduced from general principles of reason without using scientific observation, he is in complete agreement.

Still another way in which Schrödinger used the term "metaphysics" is in regard to the general properties of all things. He considered a principle such as comprehensibility to be not merely a rule of inquiry—we do not treat nature *as if* it had this characteristic—but to be a claim to represent an actual property of reality, just as Kant thought that being in space or occurring in time were both metaphysical and actual properties of all real things.

In spite of this confusion in terminology, Schrödinger was undoubtedly right in asserting that metaphysics has an important part to play if we are to give an intelligent account of even the most specialized areas of science. If we think we can do without it, we run the risk of replacing "the grand old metaphysical errors with infinitely more *naive* and petty ones."[27] The problem is to keep metaphysics within proper bounds so that it may serve as the "indispensable basis of our knowledge both general and particular" without producing unwarranted interference with the progress of science. To illustrate the apparent contradiction of

[25] *Ibid.*, p. 3.
[26] M. Polanyi, "Tacit Knowing: Its Bearing on Some Problems of Philosophy," *Revs. Mod. Phys.*, **34** (1962), 601–616.
[27] "Seek for the Road," *MVW*, p. 7.

this "uncommonly difficult task" Schrödinger used a series of images:

> We might say...that as we go forward on the road of knowledge we have *got* to let ourselves be guided by the invisible hand of metaphysics reaching out to us from the mist, but that we must always be on our guard lest its soft seductive pull should draw us from the road into an abyss. Or, to look at it another way: among the advancing hosts of the forces of knowledge, metaphysics is the vanguard, establishing the forward outposts in an unknown hostile territory; we cannot do without such outposts, but we all know that they are exposed to the most extreme danger. Or again: metaphysics does not form part of the house of knowledge but is the scaffolding, without which further construction is impossible.[28]

The most important assertion Schrödinger made about metaphysics concerns those aspects of experience that give clues about the general character of reality:

> ...phenomena of value judgment, wonder, and riddle-finding, which do not refer to any particular aspect of experience but to experience as a whole, and furthermore have impressed themselves not on idiots, but on highly competent minds, seem to me to indicate that we encounter, in our experience, relationships which have never (at least so far), even in their general form, been grasped either by formal logic or, still less, by exact science: relationships which keep forcing us back towards metaphysics; that is, towards something that transcends what is directly accessible to experience—however much we may flourish a death-certificate bearing no less valid a signature than that of Kant himself.[29]

The "death-certificate" refers, of course, to the demonstration that the particular character of things cannot be deduced from general principles of reason. The alternative to such deduction is usually considered to be induction, the act of generalizing from particular instances to rules holding for all cases. Schrödinger pointed out that acceptance of the inductive mode of reasoning involves the prior belief in the existence of regularities. He declared that induction is derived from a view of the world which has itself, logically, to be founded on induction and that therefore we have to "borrow" induction from the future results of its use.[30] He might have simply asserted what he evidently believed: induction has a metaphysical basis in the belief in comprehensibility.

[28] *Ibid.*, pp. 4–5.

[29] *Ibid.*, p. 11.

[30] Karl Popper in *The Logic of Scientific Discovery* (New York: Basic Books, 1959) has given a clear description of the difficulty of forming any consistent logic of induction.

Schrödinger's view of the relation between theory and observation may be summarized by saying that we seek a comprehensible picture of the world that is revealed to us by observation and experiment. Formal methods using inductive and deductive logic are, of course, essential, but Schrödinger indicated that we must go beyond them in more intuitive ways if we are to achieve comprehensible pictures of the whole and even of particular events.

Scientific method, Schrödinger believed, is not so far removed from methods of inquiry in other fields. Let us consider his comparison of science and history. From data an historian accepts as valid, he seeks to construct a picture of events in the past. The scientist also seeks a picture, but because he attempts to use prediction or repetition as a means of corroboration, we can easily lose sight of the fact that his desire for comprehension is essentially like that of the historian.

> It seems to me that what we are striving for here (in physics) as well as there (in history) is a comprehensive picture of the subject under investigation, a picture which becomes ever more distinct, lucid, and clearly understood in its interrelations. Here, as there, the coherence would be utterly destroyed if we felt bound by pangs of conscience to omit all that is not directly ascertained or cannot, if so desired, be confirmed by sense perceptions; if we felt bound to formulate all propositions in such a way that their relations to sense perceptions were immediately manifest.[31]

Scientific and historical method may be further compared with respect to the way in which a man's knowledge in either field depends largely on documents which describe the observations and thoughts of others, and only to a very small extent on first-hand observations. It is just in this way, in fact, that the comprehended world becomes a "world in common." In a delightful popular article on the foundations of scientific knowledge,[32] Schrödinger asserted that all science is based on the acceptance of a certain hypothesis which if tested "scientifically" would be proven false! Contrary to popular belief, the fact is that a scientist does not verify most of the information he possesses and utilizes except for that obtained in the actual research he undertakes himself. Instead, he derives his knowledge from books, articles, lectures, and conversations with other scientists. He would not trust any of these sources if he did not believe in the existence and reliability of the persons

[31] "On the Peculiarity of the Scientific World View," *WIL*, p. 197; *WN*, p. 48.
[32] "Quelques remarques au sujet des bases de la connaissance scientifique," *Scientia*, **57** (1935), 181–191.

117

who composed them. Schrödinger's hypothesis is simply that persons exist. Although "objective" tests of the stimulus-response type could verify the existence of a reacting organism, Schrödinger did not believe they could scientifically prove the existence of a *person*, capable of responsible judgments.

Although Schrödinger was joking about the existence of persons, he was correct in his interpretation of the place of the community in scientific knowledge. A physicist is actually unable to verify any but a very small part of the physics he holds to be valid. He lacks the necessary experimental or theoretical skills, apparatus, money, and assistance for anything but work in his own special field. Furthermore, in the area of his specialty, it would be an improper use of time to go through all the painstaking work needed to verify a result which he believes to have been adequately verified by others. His share of the verification process which must be carried on if we are to have a world in common is reduced to those very few results which are not yet sufficiently verified and which are within his competency to test. His main interest and duty lie in seeking new knowledge, not in verifying the old.

All scientists, in fact all scholars, are in the same position. We share in a community of trust, believing the documents we accept on the combined authority of the institutions that issue them, the editors and their referees that accept them for publication, the readers whose fields overlap those of the writers in question and who can be counted on to object to errors they find, and so forth.[33]

The scientific community is not only the depository of scientific knowledge but also acts to mold it by means of fashions of thought which govern the selection of experiments and the evaluation of theoretical developments as interesting and fruitful. Sometimes the emergence of a new theory will suddenly change the fashion and lead to the performing of experiments previously considered quite uninteresting, as when Einstein and Debye made a quantum theory of the vibrational energies of crystals, and experiments on crystal elastic constants took on a new significance.

Even the wider community in which the scientific is imbedded—the entire cultural milieu—influences science and, consequently, our comprehension of the world. This claim was made by Schrödinger in

[33] M. Polanyi has provided excellent accounts of the function of the scientific community in *Personal Knowledge* (Chicago: University of Chicago Press, 1958), p. 163 and pp. 216–220.

"Physical Science and the Temper of the Age" and "Is Science a Fashion of the Times?" For instance, Schrödinger believed that revolution and change in society are reflected in the spirit of seeking radically new ideas in science. The style of simplicity in architecture and design and the effort to simplify theories by reducing their postulates to as few statements as possible are both indications of the same "fashion of the times."[34]

Scientific activity is not only communal but emotional. Schrödinger expressed the emotional basis for scientific activity in terms of play and sport in an article that first appeared in an English language collection of his essays.[35] He asserted that when animals and men find time left over from the struggle for existence, for instance in periods of plentiful supply of food and other necessities, they use their excess energies in playful activity. Expressions of curiosity about nature are one example of such play; carried to considerable lengths of effort and thought, such expressions of curiosity produce science or, in the widest sense, scholarship. The combative aspect of sport and play finds its counterpart in science in the spirit of criticism and challenge, without which the scientific community could not function.

Schrödinger might have gone further, as Michael Polanyi has, in relating the communal and the emotional aspects of science. Polanyi has described clearly the convivial sharing and stimulation of the intellectual passion for comprehension.[36] The motives that underly science involve the search for logical consistency, the desire for elegance and simplicity in theory, the concern that deductions from theory agree with experiment, and the wish to relate as many different types of observation as possible in the framework of a single theory.

In summary, the scientist's search for comprehension is a highly motivated personal urge to discover rationality in nature, a search which is shared by a community of trust with a long history reaching back to ancient Ionia. The concrete aim of this search is a set of logical, elegant, simple pictures of nature, pictures that we rely on because they are in agreement with the perceptions made and verified by scientists whom their fellows deem reliable.

Schrödinger's hope for a future development of quantum mechanics

[34] "Is Science a Fashion of the Times?" and "Physical Science and the Temper of the Age," *STM*, pp. 81–105 and 106–132.
[35] "Science, Art, and Play," *STM*, pp. 27–38.
[36] M. Polanyi, *Personal Knowledge*, p. 133.

119

that would constitute "a return to the classical physics of clearly comprehensible events" (Ch. IV above) is an expression of his own passion for discovering rationality and picturability in nature, as well as his acceptance of the basic desire of the scientific community to remain open to new insights and to reject any principles of defeat that put limits on our ultimate vision and insight. Let us turn now to his views on the content of comprehensible pictures, particularly in physics.

5. CAUSALITY AND CHANCE AS MODES OF COMPREHENSIBILITY

Schrödinger believed that the two prime keys to the meaning of comprehensibility are *that experience can be ordered* and that *all details of a given area of experience can be derived from certain characteristic features*.[37] These two ideas implied for him that comprehensible explanations must to a large extent be causal explanations; however, he felt that equally comprehensible explanations can be formulated for certain phenomena by using the concept of chance. Schrödinger considered the concepts of causality and chance as having a central place in understanding the world. What do these ideas mean and how did Schrödinger use them?

It is not easy to give a concise summary of the concept of causality in the face of the many meanings of the term[38] and the extensive discussion in the philosophical literature. In the first place, the roots of the idea of cause and effect are in our own experience of making decisions, exerting forces, and producing effects. Thus the concept of *force* in physics has an anthropomorphic origin. Hume, Kirchhoff, and Mach focussed attention on the desirability of removing such animism from physics[39] and considerable efforts have been made to eliminate "willful" aspects from the Newtonian causal picture.

Removing animistic elements does not, however, remove our general conviction that every event must have a cause, a conviction which we derive from the experience of finding causes for effects nearly every time that we are able to analyze an event in sufficient detail.

[37] "On the Peculiarity of the Scientific World View," *WIL*, p. 183; *WN*, pp. 31–32.

[38] M. Bunge, *Causality* (Cambridge, Mass.: Harvard University Press, 1959), pp. 3–30, has an extensive discussion of definitions and meanings of "causality," "determinism," and related concepts.

[39] See E. Schrödinger, "On the Peculiarity of the Scientific World View," *WIL* pp. 188–190; *WN*, pp. 38–39.

...hand-in-hand with the discovery of *special* regular connections, we come to the idea of a *general necessary* connectedness between one phenomenon and others as an abstraction from the mass of connections as a whole. Above and beyond our actual experience, the general postulate is laid down that in those cases in which we have not yet succeeded in isolating the causal source of any specific phenomenon, such a source must surely exist—in other words, that every natural process or event is absolutely and quantitatively determined, at least through the totality of the circumstances or physical conditions that accompany its appearance. This postulate is sometimes called the "principle of causality." Our belief in it has been steadily confirmed again and again by the progressive discovery of causes that specially condition each event.[40]

Causality as used in physics is primarily a matter of differential equations, derived from application of Newton's equation $F = ma$ (and corresponding equations for electromagnetic fields) to specific systems. The solutions of such equations allow one to find the coordinates of a system at all times if the positions and velocities (or respectively, charges, currents, and fields) are all given at one initial time.[41] Schrödinger's characteristic features for such a description are the number and type of coordinates in the equations and the special values of the parameters that appear in them—masses, force constants, structural proportions, etc.

Schrödinger's teacher Franz Exner pointed out[42] that the evidence we have for the validity of $F = ma$ is derived from experience of objects containing huge numbers of atoms, where the effects of their statistical behavior are averaged out. The basic equations from which the idea of a causally-determined universe were derived are thus seen to have only a relative and limited degree of validity. It is not only or even primarily a question of whether the particular equation $F = ma$ is correct, but whether phenomena fit *any* mathematical relation precisely. An extreme example, which shows the importance of this question, is that of applying Newtonian mechanics to a toy balloon full of gas at ordinary temperature and pressure, on the assumption that the molecules are "classical," i.e., nonquantum particles. The Newtonian equations state that if we know for every particle at time $t = 0$ the three coordinates of the initial position and the three components of the initial velocity, then the motion of these particles for all later time can in principle be determined.

[40] E. Schrödinger, "What is a Law of Nature?" *STM*, p. 135; *WN*, p. 10.
[41] This view of causality is well formulated by H. Margenau, *The Nature of Physical Reality* (New York: McGraw-Hill, 1950), pp. 397–411.
[42] E. Schrödinger, *STM*, pp. 133–135; *WN*, pp. 9–11; see Ch.II, p. 31.

Let us suppose that all of the needed values for $t = 0$ are given to four significant figures, that is, with an error of about 1 in 10,000. If the demon who Laplace proposed as being a knower of all such information, as well as being a computer of infinite rapidity, had all the necessary information for such a balloon-full of gas written in books the size of large dictionaries, they would occupy a shelf roughly three light-years long. Let us however sidestep that problem and assume that the demon knows all this information in some mysterious direct and instinctive way. Consider what happens to its accuracy as collisions take place in the course of time. The errors in each set of values combine at every collision in such a way that, roughly speaking, the values for each particle afterward have $\sqrt{2}$ times the error they had before. Now, since $\sqrt{2}$ to the 27th power is 11,585, the accuracy of our set of data will be completely gone after 27 collisions for each particle, if not before. However, the mean rate of collisions for one particle in ordinary air is about one billion per second. For this extreme example, the theory has scarcely any predictive value whatever, and any other equation than $F = ma$ that requires similar initial conditions would lead to the same conclusion.

It will be objected that absolute accuracy is possible in principle. Let us be practical again. The number of significant figures needed to make the above prediction valid for just one second is about 150,000,000. There is no evidence of a scientific nature that would justify claims that Newton's law $F = ma$ or any other equation is valid to that accuracy.

Newton's theory has so far been most precisely verified in the mechanics of the solar system; here the accuracy is roughly to a mere six figures. The situation in astronomy is the opposite extreme from that of molecular motions in a gas, for the high degree of separation of the planets and the infrequency of collisions with even small objects allow prediction to have relatively high accuracy for thousands of years. Most terrestrial phenomena, such as the weather, are far too complex to be treated like either of these simple examples, although weather predictions are made by computers using the Newtonian mechanics of fluid motion. Recent developments have given hope that the range of accurate prediction might be extended from the present few hours to possibly a week with statistical prediction for another week. There is, however, little likelihood of ever getting beyond a few weeks' prediction, for reasons related to the propagation of error in the simple gas model just described.

Schrödinger described our situation with respect to the limitations of strictly causal explanations in a particularly thoughtful way. He noted our focus of attention on "causal chains" and our tendency to overlook as scientifically meaningless their accidental intersections.[43] A causal chain is a series of events which we could explain in strictly deterministic manner. Each lasts in general for only a limited period of time, or at least our knowledge of it is so limited. Since we rarely analyze any particular chain explicitly, we do not have a clear definition of what is causal and what is accidental.[44] Thus we can not say just when prediction would become meaningless.

The intersections of such causal chains are treated by Schrödinger as examples of completely "chance" events. In spite of their constant occurrence and their relevance to daily life, there is no systematic way of treating such intersections, either inside or outside of science. An example is the occurrence of a storm near Yorktown toward the end of the American Revolution. One chain of events led to the British being at Yorktown, surrounded by American and French forces. Another chain of events led to the development of that particular storm and the resulting inability of the British to evacuate troops to the north. This coincidence, which Schrödinger would call a chance intersection, led to the surrender of Cornwallis and ultimately to the end of the war.[45]

I shall come back to the idea of intersecting causal chains in the discussion of human determinism in the next section. Suffice it to say here that the idea of chance coincidence could not arise without our first having an idea of causality with which to contrast it, and that the idea of a causal chain could not exist without a well-founded world picture that tells us what sort of things to leave out as not causally effective within our chosen degree of accuracy.

Such chance intersections are listed by Schrödinger among the "gaps left by the hypothesis of comprehensibility."[46] A religiously or mystically oriented person is inclined to seek an "explanation" for what seems to be an accidental occurrence, whereas a scientist would prefer to leave it unexplained, hoping that further developments in science will fill the gap,

[43] "On the Peculiarity of the Scientific World View," *WIL*, pp. 201–202; *WN*, pp. 52–54.

[44] D. Bohm, *Causality and Chance in Modern Physics* (Princeton: D. Van Nostrand, 1957), pp. 1–3, makes the distinction between causal and contingent effects clear and straightforward.

[45] This example was given by Ernest Nagel in a speech at Amherst College on the problem of determinism in history.

[46] "On the Peculiarity of the Scientific World View," *WIL*, pp. 200–206; *WN*, pp. 52–58.

rather than risk betraying his goal of achieving a scientific picture of nature by imposing a nonscientific explanation on such experience.

In addition to the use of the concept of chance in describing single accidental events without explaining them, the concept functions as a foundation for exploration of regularities in two highly developed ways in physics and biology. Schrödinger discusses these two other applications as positive features of the scientific world picture, embodying what he called "intelligible chance." Although these applications of the idea of chance to explain regularity are quite different from the first use, they all have in common, as Schrödinger says, the scientific principle that "chance is just chance."

In physics the use of chance appears in statistical mechanics; it is our heritage from Boltzmann. First, we assume certain statistical laws[47] for individual atomic collisions or other events. Then we apply the rules of counting and the law of large numbers. And behold, regular behavior for large bodies of gas or liquid and for large solid objects results. Furthermore, we not only come out with Newtonian physics as a good approximation for the macroscopic world, we can explain its failures for small objects, e.g., for the random Brownian motion of microscopic bacteria that are bombarded by water molecules on all sides but not quite uniformly.[48]

Statistical mechanics provides an ordered description of several aspects of the physical world and involves characteristic features such as temperature, pressure, volume, number of molecules, compressibility, and other large-scale measures of material properties. Even without an underlying hypothesis of causality, statistical mechanics extends comprehensibility to the areas of physics with which it deals. Schrödinger noted that statistical mechanics exemplifies the concept of intelligible chance.[49]

Can we also say that statistical mechanics provides a *picture* of nature? It might seem that this would be the case only if the individual processes were causal and themselves picturable. However, I venture to suggest that no one can really picture, even in principle, 10^{23} molecules in collision. But picturability to the finest detail of resolution is beside the

---

[47] We could start with causal laws, but we need a statistical assumption about the randomness of collisions, etc.

[48] See M. Born, *Natural Philosophy of Cause and Chance* (London: Oxford University Press, 1949), pp. 62–65 and 170–176.

[49] "On the Peculiarity of the Scientific World View," *WIL*, p. 199; *WN*, pp. 48–49.

point. A mental image of collective behavior that does not try to "resolve" individual molecules nevertheless serves physicists very well in a practical way. If in addition there is an awareness of how this collective behavior is related to underlying regularity even of a statistical nature, the resulting view will satisfy Schrödinger's definition of a comprehensible picture. It will then be only in respect to *picturable* individual events which follow a statistical law of chance that a "gap" in comprehensibility remains.

Schrödinger clearly felt that statistical mechanics is comprehensible, but he rejected as incomprehensible an interpretation of quantum mechanics that assumes an irreducibly statistical behavior of material particles. Insofar as he was referring to the inability of quantum mechanics to predict individual events, this judgment is consistent with his views about comprehensibility and the gaps in it. But insofar as quantum mechanics deals with ensembles in a way similar to statistical mechanics, Schrödinger's conflicting attitudes are not easy to understand. (See Ch. IV for a detailed discussion.)

The concept of complementarity as now used in quantum mechanics to handle the statistical difficulties is probably a historically conditioned idea. Perhaps after physicists become thoroughly accustomed to all the "queer" things that happen in atomic systems, their sense of surprise and contradictoriness will disappear, and there will be no gaps in comprehensibility left to be resolved by calling them "complementary."

Another area in which the laws of chance provide a picturable theory is that of Darwinian evolution. Schrödinger considered the theory of biological evolution the second great application of statistical ideas to the understanding of nature. Here we have the simple idea that, when many more individuals of a given species are born than can survive to reproduce, small selective advantages of the environment will in the long run favor modifications in the species that fit in with these advantages. This idea was enlarged by De Vries' idea of mutations and by Mendel's laws of heredity.[50]

The resulting theory of evolution is a profoundly interesting example of intelligible chance. Chance has produced the intelligence that can

---

[50] As Schrödinger points out in "The Spirit of Science" (*WIL*, pp. 238–239), the removal of Mendel's writings from obscurity by three independent discoverers and the publication of De Vries' theory of mutations occurred at just about the time that Planck discovered the quantum of action. Only much later did these two great theories become related, as I shall discuss in the next section.

comprehend it and can see that it is indeed intelligible! In 1950, in a series of three BBC broadcasts,[51] Schrödinger discussed an aspect of evolution that illustrates the "intelligibility" of chance in reference to the possibility of further evolution of the human brain. He suggested that even though our rate of evolution has been considerably slowed down by our medical arts, which when looked at from a purely evolutionary point of view result in "an indiscriminate saving of lives," there still may be a tendency to favor intelligent over stupid behavior. Although behavior is not inherited—the Lamarckian theory of the inheritance of acquired characteristics has been discredited—the process of chance mutations and preferential survival can give the *appearance* of the inheritance of acquired behavior patterns.

Schrödinger's argument was taken from Julian Huxley[52] and runs approximately as follows: In a given species a certain chance mutation may occur to favor the survival of individuals in an environment which they had previously not tended to visit frequently. If further mutations occur which happen to alter their behavior in such a way that they spend more time in this newly-favorable environment, there will be a tendency to select individuals carrying both the original mutation and the mutations that change their behavior. Consequently a group of individuals will come to live most of their time in the new environment, so that further mutations favoring life in this area will be selected. The final appearance will be that the behavior of the ancestors in first going to this environment is "inherited," and furthermore that the original change of behavior is speeded by evolution.

Schrödinger believed that our brains may evolve if we favor intelligent behavior and arrange for that "interesting and intelligent competition of the single human beings" that may continue as an active selection process. On the other hand, he feared that the "increasing mechanization and 'stupidization' of most manufacturing processes" would lead to the demise of any such selective process, so that the general preponderance of degenerative mutations would result in a progressive degeneration of our brains. He suggested that men should do the interesting work themselves, leaving dull routine work to machines, even if it costs more.[53]

[51] "The Future of Understanding," Sept, 16, 23, and 30, 1950. Reprinted in *WIL*, pp. 118–131 and also as Ch. II of *MM*.

[52] J. Huxley, *Evolution, The Modern Synthesis* (New York: Harper, 1943), pp. 497–501.

[53] *WIL*, pp. 130–131; *MM*, pp. 34–35.

(Perhaps there is biological as well as economic justification for automation.)

While this theory of brain evolution is a rather specialized example, it nevertheless serves to indicate the "intelligible" functions of a process based on chance. The question of the relative roles of causality and chance in individual living organisms leads us to Schrödinger's concern with the explanation of living systems.

6. COMPREHENSIBILITY IN LIVING SYSTEMS

Biological processes seem, at least superficially, to be comprehensible only in terms of concepts and laws that are quite distinct from those of present-day physics and chemistry. Schrödinger wrote *What is Life?* with the expressed aim of coming to grips with the question: "How can the events *in space and time* which take place within the spatial boundary of a living organism be accounted for by physics and chemistry?"[54] Although a great deal of effort has been made to answer this question since 1943, the central points he made still appear to be relevant.

The ordinary physics and chemistry of macroscopic objects derive regularity from the disordered behavior of the underlying atomic substratum by means of the statistical smoothing-out which occurs with large numbers of atoms and molecules. The first point Schrödinger made about life is that the relation of the macroscopic to the atomic is to a large extent that of order being derived from order, rather than from random behavior. The key to this relation is the regular but nonrepeating arrangement of atoms which Schrödinger called an "aperiodic crystal."[55]

An aperiodic crystal, as Schrödinger used the term, is an arrangement of atoms which is definite, ordered, and stable (as in an ordinary crystal), but which (in contrast to an ordinary crystal) does not contain repetitions of a smaller unit. To put it another way, the unit cell of the aperiodic crystal is the entire molecule, and there is no arbitrariness about its size. The genetic code which determines the growth, form, and structure of a living organism appears to be carried by such molecules. Life processes derive their order from aperiodic crystals, assisted by the statistically regulated physical and chemical behavior of disordered molecules in the liquid and gas phases.

[54] *WIL*, p. 2.
[55] *WIL*, p. 3, and pp. 60–61.

Schrödinger devoted a good part of *What is Life?* to outlining the main features of the genetic mechanism as it was known in 1943. The information content of the genetic code is passed on with only very rare small mutations, not only to every cell of one organism but also to the germ cells which pass on portions of the information content from each parent into the code for each offspring. Whereas the aperiodic crystals of the genetic code carry far more information than do ordinary periodic crystals, they do not have quite as much thermal stability. To study the stability and the mutability of the genetic material, it is essential to consider the role of quantum theory, which is the second of Schrödinger's main points about the nature of life.

The stability of the genetic code is most remarkable. Our ancestors have looked like human beings for probably a million years, all because of these molecules which produce others that are *very nearly* identical with themselves in a continuous stream of succession passed on from parents to offspring from the very beginning of life. Classical chemistry and physics could not account for such stability, for there was no reason why random heat motion should not produce a continuing statistical variation in pattern.

The high degree of stability in ordinary periodic crystals is explained in quantum mechanics by a postulate about the activation energy necessary to raise members of the crystal array out of their ordered positions. However, living substance is not so stable. Mutations, i.e., molecular rearrangements that modify the code, *are* possible and occur at rates suitable for evolution. Furthermore, nucleic acids and proteins, the basic compounds of cell and tissue structures, have a relative degree of stability that leads them to persist in certain chemical environments but to break down in others.[56]

Schrödinger discussed evidence concerning the nature of mutations and their frequency of occurrence. Most mutations produce effects which are harmful to vital processes; furthermore, the rate of mutation is such that two rarely occur in one individual. If several mutations occurred in one individual, the rare beneficial ones would be overwhelmed by the nonviable ones. In fact, it takes several generations for a "good" mutation to establish itself in a population, even when it is unaccompanied by

[56] Dorothy Wrinch has described well this "stab-lab" property—proteins are stable in some circumstances and labile (changeable) in others. See "Native Protein Structure in the Light of Physico-Chemical Findings," *Experimental Medicine and Surgery*, **13** (1955), p. 36.

harmful ones. We may conclude that evolution of the hereditary mechanism has eliminated tendencies to too-rapid mutation.

It is also noteworthy that a mutated gene is in most cases (but not all) as stable with respect to further mutation as it was before the mutation. We have then to explain a low rate of transfer between molecular arrangements of similar stability (and therefore similar potential energy, since the relation between the mean thermal energy[57] kT and the potential energy of the arrangement is the basic one that accounts for stability). The explanation furnished by quantum theory is that a high energy barrier, analogous to a mountain ridge between two valleys, lies between each pair of possible arrangements. A transfer requires the absorption of enough energy for the system to cross the top of the barrier.[58]

The observed low rate of mutation is accounted for by assuming an appropriate value W of the energy needed to get over the barrier. When the mean energy available per atom is kT, statistical considerations allow one to calculate the probability that an energy W much larger than kT be acquired by atoms at the specific location needed to initiate a mutation. The frequency of transfers over a barrier of height W turns out to be roughly proportional to the quantity $e^{-W/kT}$ which can readily be fitted to the observed rate by proper choice of W. Thus quantum mechanics contributes to an explanation of the form and stability of living systems, while at the same time it supplements statistical mechanics to furnish an understanding of the degree of chance involved in evolutionary mutations.

Schrödinger discussed the role of chance and disorder in the processes within a single individual. Besides the ordering mechanism of the genetic code, an organism contains liquid systems and takes in and gives off various gases. To what extent do the physical and chemical laws relevant to nonliving fluids apply to life? In particular, do living things follow the regular process whereby randomness is increased and order reduced, summarized by the Second Law of Thermodynamics?

A measure of the increase of randomness in any system is the rate of increase of entropy (see Ch. II). In physics and chemistry, this process is

[57] See any standard physics text.

[58] This description seems to justify the idea of quantum jumps that was shown to be invalid in the previous chapter. However, a mutation does not have to be instantaneous—Schrödinger's continuous type of description could be applied to the combination of transition of the wave function over the barrier and the "materialization" of the system in the new position, very much as a cloud chamber track is described.

frequently seen as the approach to equilibrium, which for a living system can only mean death and decay. Schrödinger's point is that living systems fight the approach to equilibrium by acquiring ordered materials from their environment which have low entropy values. Plants furthermore acquire high-energy photons from the sun, involving especially low entropy values, i.e., large amounts of negative entropy. These large quantities of negative entropy are passed on to animals that consume them.

Thus Schrödinger proposed that we eat food primarily as a source of negative entropy, rather than energy, although in a note added to section VI of *What is Life?* he pointed out that the particular form of the food-stuff is, of course, important and also that the energy is needed because the radiation of bodily heat is a means of getting rid of generated positive entropy. It is beyond my competence to evaluate these comments about the value of food, but it seems clear that the over-all picture of entropy balance is correct.

The final important question of *What is Life?* concerns the behavior of a living being. Is behavior determined? Does an organism operate like a mechanism?

Schrödinger did not discuss in detail the mechanism of the nervous system in providing for perception, thought, and muscular control. Instead, he provided an image: an organism bears a strong resemblance to a clock. A good clock is a mechanism in which the disordering effects of friction do not noticeably interfere with its regularity. Similarly, the disordering, entropy-producing features in organic life do not create any appreciable interference with its ordered behavior. In accordance with the Nernst heat theorem which says, in effect, that ordered systematic behavior appears in atomic systems as the temperature approaches absolute zero (i.e., as kT gets too small for disorder to occur frequently), Schrödinger describes life processes as going on at "nearly absolute zero." That is, our body temperature, about $310°$ on the absolute Kelvin scale, is "small" compared to temperatures that would produce disorder. This assertion about the closeness to absolute zero must be taken with caution, however, because on the one hand, life processes must be described in terms of non-equilibrium statistical mechanics, and on the other hand, these processes are of such complexity that the ordinary chemical rules about the effects of increased temperature do not apply. One cannot associate a single temperature with a system far from equilibrium, nor can one safely infer that it would take a large increase of temperature to destroy our ordered behavior—we know that in fact only a few degrees will suffice.

Nevertheless, Schrödinger was right in saying that as organisms we are highly ordered and apparently deterministic mechanisms. The question arises as to whether causality can be applied without limit to living beings or whether chance also enters. It should be clear from the discussion of causality in the previous section that all we should hope to comprehend within a living organism is a series of organized interlocking causal chains of events. Schrödinger himself did not apply his notion of causal chains to the human body, asserting that the body functions as a "pure mechanism."[59] However, it seems illogical to rule out the possibility of chance events having an influence on the behavior of an organism. Organisms function by many processes of adaptation and there is every reason to assume that accidental intersections of causal chains, particularly in brain processes, play an important role in the development of individuality, for instance by determining which ideas come to mind first when one is trying to solve a problem.

If this is so, do such chance events play any role in explaining free will? The question has often arisen in connection with Heisenberg's principle of indeterminacy. Schrödinger himself did not believe that the explanation of free will is in any way enhanced by the possibility that chance events play a role in life, and his several arguments seem to be sound.[60]

Schrödinger's argument starts by showing that the major role of quantum theory in life processes is different from that assigned by the Heisenberg principle. In *What is Life?* he described the way quantum effects lead to stability rather than indeterminacy in the maintenance of the genetic code of living organisms, (i.e., in the long intervals between chance mutations). Quantum effects also function in the definite on-off quality of single nerve impulses, although Schrödinger did not take up their quantum aspects. Every nerve sends impulses which are all of a definite size. Either they go, or they do not; only their rate is variable.[61] The concept of transition between two quantum levels separated by a potential barrier thus is also applicable here. If quantum uncertainty plays a role, it does not seem to function in the control processes accessible to study.

---

[59] *WIL*, p. 85.
[60] In contrast, H. Margenau describes freedom as a combination of chance and choice in *Open Vistas* (New Haven: Yale University Press, 1961), pp. 207–214.
[61] *WIL*, pp. 46–56.

Schrödinger's second argument[62] is that the Heisenberg uncertainty rule is a statistical rule. If choice is to be explained by some kind of operation of this rule, a statistic of resulting actions will appear, which could then by further choice be modified and the statistic invalidated. In the third place, Schrödinger approved Cassirer's point[63] that free will implies responsible action, and therefore *ordered control* of one's actions. Any postulate implying randomness can be introduced only at the cost of losing this element of ordered control and hence of free will and moral responsibility. Summarizing his position, Schrödinger wrote:

> The net result is that quantum physics has nothing to do with the free-will problem. If there is such a problem, it is not furthered to a whit by the latest development in physics. To quote Ernst Cassirer again: "Thus it is clear— that a possible change in the physical concept of causality can have no immediate bearing on ethics."[64]

There remains the question initially posed by Schrödinger. Can the observed behavior of living organisms be accounted for in terms of the laws of physics and chemistry? The four points discussed above—the aperiodic crystal, the stabilizing role of quantized energy levels, the intake of negative entropy, and the clocklike mechanism—amount to physical principles of a limiting or conditioning type. They do not account in detail for either genetics or behavior. To the question whether the details can be handled by physics or chemistry, Schrödinger's answer would be, "Yes, but not yet."[65] He believed that new laws of physics, not laws of a realm of science alien to physics, would be needed to handle the order-from-order problem.

What sort of laws would these be? Schrödinger described them as laws concerning the operation of a construction of matter different from that which we have yet treated in physics and chemistry.[66] In fact, recent developments provide clues to such new laws. They are not always called laws of *physics*, however. Sometimes the term "molecular biophysics" is used, sometimes "molecular biology," and often the older term "biochemistry."

In any case, Schrödinger's view appears, at first sight, to be reductive.

[62] *Nature*, **138** (1936), 13–14.

[63] From E. Cassirer, *Determinism and Indeterminism in Modern Physics*, trans. by O. T. Benfey (New Haven: Yale University Press, 1956) Ch. 13, as quoted by E. Schrödinger, *SH*, pp., 207–208.

[64] *SH*, p. 67.

[65] *WIL*, p. 2.

[66] *WIL*, pp. 74–80.

By any reasonable definition, physics and chemistry have limited applicability. It seems unwise to identify all scientific laws which are related even indirectly to physics and chemistry as belonging to these disciplines. The natural and social sciences can be loosely arranged in a hierarchy of complexity with physics at the bottom[67] and psychology and sociology at the top. There are no theoretical systems at present which claim to derive the principles of the higher sciences from those of the lower ones. The common assertion that such a derivation is possible in principle is based on what I believe to be a wrong assumption, namely that reality consists of *nothing but* the atoms and molecules studied in physics and chemistry. Such an assertion denies reality to patterns of form and organization, patterns which play a central role in life processes. A view of reality that considers all things and happenings to be reducible to the motions of individual particles is a view which not only would make the nature of life a mystery, but which would leave the self out completely.

Michael Polanyi has a view of the relations of the sciences which avoids this reductionism and provides a basis for a meaningful critique of Schrödinger's "Yes, but not yet." According to Polanyi, physics deals with atoms and molecules, and bodies made of these, without dealing with details of chemical combination. Chemistry involves the concepts of element, compound, and mixture, to which laws of physics can be made to apply only after these substances have been recognized and classified by essentially chemical procedures.

Engineering involves a tremendous variety of contrivances, using materials and laws studied in chemistry and physics but organized around functional principles which themselves are not to be found anywhere in these two basic disciplines. For instance, a clockwork involves the physical principles of levers, gears, oscillating motion, and so forth, but a machine can only be defined and recognized as a clockwork by bringing in the organizing engineering principle—that of an escapement providing for regular motion as a consequence of a controlled systematic release of stored energy.

A watch cannot be described by means of laws of physics and chemistry and the principle of clockwork, for the further principles of a symbolic system for communicating the time and a method of verifying its accuracy in terms of cultural conventions and astronomical observations must be included if we are to say what we mean by the word "watch."

---

[67] Schrödinger referred to physics as the "humblest of sciences," *MM*, p. 103.

Similarly, the organizing principles involved in systems of biochemical reactions, in the system for storing and transmitting the genetic code, in the structure and function of living cells, in tissues, organs and organisms, are successively more involved as we consider higher sciences in the biological dimension of the hierarchy.

The various sciences actually use whatever organizing principles are relevant to their subject matter. However, the claim that these can be "derived" from lower levels of organization, and ultimately from physics, is spurious.

In the light of the above analysis, it appears that Schrödinger's claim about new laws of physics and chemistry which may appear in biology is largely a matter of terminology. If the terms "physics and chemistry" are to keep roughly their present meaning, Schrödinger's prediction should be interpreted to mean that new organizing principles will be found that go beyond the laws of physics and chemistry but are not in contradiction to these laws. One can go further and say that the present laws of physics and chemistry, especially quantum mechanics, form essential *conditions* which limit the form and range of application of any new laws we expect to find in biology. The freedom allowed within these limits for biological development could be described in terms of physics as the range of possible initial or boundary values. In systems as complex as organisms, this range of freedom is very great indeed.

In *Mind and Matter, My View of the World*, and the article "On the Peculiarity of the Scientific World View," Schrödinger discussed three other questions concerning the spatio-temporal understanding of life. The first question is closely related to that of free will: Where or how does mind act on matter? The second is: What determines the qualities of our sensations? and the third, what events in space and time correspond to consciousness?

In discussion of the first question, the role of mind in bodily functions, Schrödinger refers repeatedly to Charles Sherrington, who has described the search for this role in his magnificently written and thoroughly honest book, *Man on his Nature*.[68] As Sherrington reports his search, there turns out to be *no place* in the nervous system or elsewhere in the body where mind acts on matter. "Mind per se cannot play the piano—mind per se cannot move a finger of a hand"[69] nor induce brain cells to trans-

---

[68] C. Sherrington, *Man on His Nature* (2nd edition; Cambridge: Cambridge University Press, 1951).

[69] *Ibid.*, p. 222; "On the Peculiarity of Scientific World View," *WIL*, p. 215; *WN*, p. 68.

mit impulses. Either mind *is* matter, he says, or by its very meaning it cannot act on matter, for the concept "matter" *means* that which we perceive by its action on other matter.

Note that it would be a mistake to characterize Sherrington's view of physiology, which Schrödinger shared, by saying "we know *that* mind acts on the body, but not *how* it acts." All we can say is that if a person decides to do something, e.g., rise from his chair, a decision-making part of his mind acts on a muscle-commanding part of his mind, or equally that the central cortex of the brain acts on nerves and muscles. There is no way to have an *additional* effect of mind on these same nerves and muscles.

Not only can we find no place where mind acts on matter, but no way in which matter acts directly on mind. Of course sense perceptions are used in science, but the observer is removed from direct influence as much as possible. He functions as a pointer-reader, but his subjective experience is (presumably) left out of the account in analyzing experimental results. Schrödinger devoted the last chapter of *Mind and Matter* to considering what determines the quality of our sensations. Drawing from his excursion of 1920 into theories of color vision, he lucidly described the physics and physiology of sight and hearing and remarked on the character of taste and smell. The burden of his account is exactly that of Democritus (quoted above in sec. 3), that no matter how far we go in scientific investigation, we never explain the sensations of yellow and red, harmony and discord, bitter and sweet, or any other direct perception. There is no way in which the stimuli of perception can have a special action on the mind in addition to their biological action.

If mind cannot act on matter, nor matter on mind, and if in some way mind and matter are identical with each other, the question of what material processes correspond to, or lead to, consciousness becomes acute. Does all matter have mental properties, or is there a special distinction between "mental" and "nonmental" matter? Schrödinger described with approval the answer given to this question by Richard Semon, that consciousness is not associated with a kind of matter but with a kind of occurrence—specifically the occurrence of novelty in a biological system.[70] Consciousness is thinking new thoughts, having

---

[70] R. Semon, *Die Mneme als erhaltendes Prinzip im Wechsel des organischen Geschehens* (3rd ed., Leipzig: W. Engelmann, 1911). The possibility of confusion with Lamarckism was the reason Schrödinger gave for waiting thirty years before publishing these views on consciousness (*MM*, pp. 14–15). They were first written

experiences which we have not had before, or at least have not experienced before in exactly the same way. It is knowing that today is not yesterday. On the other hand, as behavior becomes routine and habitual, it recedes from consciousness—the completely habitual has no correlation with consciousness at all.

Schrödinger concluded that "Consciousness is associated with the *learning* of the living substance; its *knowing how* [*Können*] is unconscious."[71]

According to this view, which has been stated in other terms by Edmund Sinnott in his *Biology of the Spirit*,[72] consciousness began to appear in the course of evolution when the process of biological adaptation began. The more complex the adaptive systems, the more complex the novel situations to which they can adapt, and the more consciousness we must ascribe to them. Consciousness, in fact, becomes for the higher animals and man the most important organizing principle for comprehending them. I shall have more to say of this type of comprehension later.

7. OBJECTIVATION AND ITS CONSEQUENCES

The difficulty of finding a place where mind and matter interact is but one of the many serious consequences of objectivation with which Schrödinger was concerned. Another basic difficulty is that the very act of considering the world as "out there" leaves the observing self out of the world picture. As we construct our "world in common," Schrödinger said, "we are hypostatizing the world as an object, making the assumption of a real world around us—as the most popular phrase runs—made up of overlapping parts of our several consciousnesses. And in doing so,

---

down in "Seek for the Road" in 1925, but did not become public until the Tarner Lectures of 1956, which became the book *Mind and Matter*. It was the discovery of how Darwinian evolution can "feign a sort of sham-Lamarckism," as described in section 4 above, that made it possible to avoid this confusion.

Richard Semon tried to lump together under the term *Mneme* the three different aspects of persistence in living beings: memory, habit, and heredity. His work was, on the one hand, not grounded in physiology and on the other, not part of an ongoing school of psychology. Furthermore, his attempts to relate heredity and memory involved him in a real or apparent affirmation of the Lamarckian notion of the inheritance of acquired characteristics. As a consequence, his work has not achieved much recognition. Nevertheless, his insight into the connection between consciousness and novelty is of permanent value. Schrödinger put his finger on the right point, as he so often did.

[71] *MM*, p. 9.

[72] E. Sinnott, *The Biology of the Spirit* (New York: Viking Press, 1955), pp. 55–60.

everyone willy-nilly takes himself—the subject of cognizance, the thing that says 'cogito, ergo sum'—out of the world, removes himself from it into the position of an external observer, who does not himself belong to the party."[73]

It is not a matter, however, of the cognizing self being removed from our experience. We do indeed experience our selves as subjects, as doers and perceivers. However, the world picture cannot include the point from which it is viewed—just as a lighthouse beacon is not included in the area which it illuminates—so the knowing subject, the self, cannot be *in* the picture.

Furthermore, Schrödinger understood simultaneous awareness of the self and of the world to be mutually exclusive. If in the course of life we focus on the world out there—on the meanings of our perceptions—we indeed experience a world that is really there. If, however, we reflect on our selves in the act of perception, the *same* sensations, thoughts and feelings that are involved in perception constitute for us an experience of the self. The world and the mind "consist of the same bricks, as it were, only arranged in a different order—sense perceptions, memory, imagination, thought."[74] We can adjust our attention to the external world, or to ourselves, but it is only with great difficulty that we can focus on both simultaneously.

We do not often notice the fact that the cognizing self is left out of the world picture. In granting the existence of other selves as we usually do, we easily generate the illusion that the "I" is in the picture, too. Schrödinger discussed[75] what he called the "faulty chain of reasoning" by which the omission of the "I" is covered up: My body is part of the objective world and so are the bodies of others. Other persons seem to be just the same type of being that I am. If I believe that other persons exist as personal selves within their bodies, I assume that I exist in the same way, as objectively as do the others. I put myself back in the picture very much as an artist may sometimes paint himself into a small corner of his painting[76] or a writer include himself as a minor figure in his novel. Schrödinger considered this reasoning to be faulty, putting in the picture as *object* that which is essentially *subject*.

[73] *NG*, p. 91.
[74] *NG*, pp. 91–92.
[75] *NG*, p. 94; "On the Peculiarity of the Scientific World View," *WIL*, pp. 182–184, *WN*, pp. 33–34; *MM*, p. 38.
[76] *MM*, p. 65.

Even though we normally grant the existence of other selves, objectivation taken strictly also leaves them out of the world picture. Not only is there no biological connection between self and body, but if we try to make personality an object of scientific study, Schrödinger warns that we will find nothing but a biological mechanism:

> Nowhere...do we encounter the personality, nowhere the heartache and the anxiety that move this soul and of whose reality we are as certain as if we ourselves were suffering them—as we do. It is really true that the physiological analysis of any human being, even our closest friend, reveals the same sight to us as in E. A. Poe's masterpiece *The Masque of the Red Death* is revealed to the one who insolently tears away from the masker his cloak and domino and underneath finds—nothing. For are nerve cells and electric currents anything more, where it is for us a matter of emotional values and the experience of the soul?[77]

While we cannot approach our knowing selves as objects, we can nevertheless try to sense our relation to our own bodies by reflecting simultaneously on our experience of doing things and our knowledge of the causal or semi-causal structure of our bodies which is revealed by the study of life processes. In the epilogue to *What is Life?* Schrödinger reflected on the paradox of free will and determinism. The study of living systems leads convincingly to the notion that every act of every human being follows the law of causality, at least insofar as it is an orderly controlled action. However, our experience of free will is equally incontrovertible—there are many acts which we know that *we* do and could have done otherwise had *we* chosen. We seem to be *both* free and determined, yet how can this be?

Schrödinger concluded that each of us is somehow *identical with the causal process of all nature.* He suggested that this identity is what is meant by the Hindu declaration that Atman (the soul or personal self) is one with Brahman (God, the omnipresent, all-comprehending eternal Self.)[78] The doctrine of identity was for Schrödinger the "deep philosophical insight" that resolves the difficulties of objectivation. This concept of identity had the further paradoxical consequence for Schrödinger that in spite of the plurality of bodies there is only *one* subjective self. He tried to bolster this idea by referring to evidence that consciousness is always

[77] "On the Peculiarity of the Scientific World View," *WIL*, pp. 217–218; *WN*, p. 72.

[78] See S. N. Khilananda, *The Upanishads* (New York: Harper, 1959), IV, Chhāndogya Upanishad, vi, Chs. 8–16.

experienced in the singular. Even in cases in which the two halves of a brain seem to operate independently, there seems to be no duality of consciousness.[79] Even further, each one of us knows only our own consciousness—we never experience that of another in the same way. Schrödinger concluded that consciousness is a *singulare tantum*, something that in its very nature has no plural.

The peculiarity of many persons being one he calls the arithmetical paradox:

> The reason why our sentient, percipient and thinking ego is met nowhere within our scientific world picture can easily be indicated in seven words: because it is itself that world picture. It is identical with the whole and therefore cannot be contained in it as part of it. But, of course, here we knock against the arithmetical paradox; there appears to be a great multitude of these conscious egos, the world however is only one.[80]

An important argument that Schrödinger found for the doctrine of identity stems from a basic question about perception: Is there both a world "out there" and a world of perception formed by interaction of the former world with our minds? Schrödinger said no, the world is given to us only once.[81] Any *unobservable* world "out there" he dismissed as a Kantian *Ding an sich* that "holds no interest for us whatever...we are going, if necessary, to disregard it."[82] The world of which we speak *is* the world of perception, and this world is held in common—in fact, it is just the holding in common that convinces us it is real. But my perception appears to be uniquely mine—and not the same as that of others. Is my view the real one and are all the others illusory? Schrödinger believed that we either have to accept the belief in a real world out there and many perceived worlds, a view which he considered nonsensical, or we have to believe that there is only one perception, namely by the Self with which each one of us is numerically one. This perception *is* the world. Since the world is then somehow in the mind perceiving it, it must be identical with it if one is to avoid the difficulty of a part containing the whole.

The argument is carried further by reference to evolution. If we treat the existing world as identical with the world perceived and take mind as a latecomer to the evolutionary scene, we have the absurdity that the

[79] C. Sherrington, *op. cit.*, pp. 212–215.
[80] *MM*, p. 52.
[81] *MM*, p. 51; *WIL*, p. 225; *WN*, p. 81.
[82] "Seek for the Road," *MVW*, p. 15.

world only came into being at this late date. Or, less absurdly, that the world did not light up to itself until mind arrived. But we have the question, what happened before this awareness took place? Were the phenomena of prehuman evolution all "a play before empty seats"?[83] Was the world *then* the purely external reality we no longer say it is?[84]

All these difficulties are answered by Schrödinger's doctrine of identity. If mind is conceived as universal and identical with the world, or with the causal process as its essence, then the idea of the world gradually becoming conscious to itself is not contradictory. Schrödinger suggested that perhaps Spinoza and Fechner were not so far wrong in treating everything as a modification of God himself.[85]

The doctrine of identity is for Schrödinger the basic conviction of Vedanta philosophy.[86] For Vedanta, the plurality of selves is an illusion, the "unity of knowledge, feeling, and choice which you call *your own*... are essentially eternal and unchangeable and numerically *one* in all men, nay in all sensitive beings."[87]

Schrödinger illustrated this view in relation to the continuity of a person's conscious ego with his cultural and genetic inheritance.[88] His examples served his purposes in making this continuity clear but are not particularly convincing about the numerical unity of oneself with one's ancestors. Suppose, Schrödinger suggested, you are sitting on a hillside in an Alpine valley. Was it really you yourself, he asked, who also sat on this hillside a hundred years ago and looked at the same mountain scenery?[89]

In "Seek for the Road" Schrödinger emphasized that he did *not* mean by the unity of selves that a person is "a part, a piece, of an external, infinite being, an aspect or modification of it, as in Spinoza's pantheism."[90] In contrast, writing much later in "What is Real?" he approved the Vedanta view that "we are all in reality sides or aspects of

[83] E. Schrödinger, "On the Peculiarity of the Scientific World View," *WIL*, p. 224; *WN*, p. 81.
[84] Owen Barfield described the same problem in very similar terms in *Saving the Appearances, A Study in Idolatry* (London: Faber and Faber, 1957), esp. Ch. X.
[85] "Seek for the Road," *MVW*, p. 41.
[86] Schrödinger did not accept all of Vedanta philosophy. For instance, he rejected the theme of the transmigration of souls and the related doctrine of Karma ("What is Real?" *MVW*, p. 102).
[87] E. Schrödinger, "Seek for the Road," *MVW*, p. 21.
[88] *Ibid.*, Ch. VI.
[89] *Ibid.*, pp. 20–21.
[90] *Ibid.*, p. 21.

one single being, which may perhaps in western terminology be called God while in the Upanishads its name is Brahman."[91] However, consistent application of his ideas requires even closer identity than this, for if we are *separate* aspects of reality, we surely have separate perceptions of the world. We are brought back to the same baffling questions, as indeed Schrödinger says, following the earlier of the two quotations just given.

Schrödinger supported his idea of the universal Self, which clearly has to be timeless or eternal, with arguments showing how science has liberated us from the illusion that time is absolute. The liberation, which he termed "*the* religious thought,"[92] he ascribed primarily to the work of Plato, Kant, Einstein, Boltzmann, and Gibbs.[93]

Plato contributed the notion of the timeless existence of Forms and Ideas, and Kant the view that the world might have other orders of appearance than the particular time-like ones which we impose as we observe it. Einstein showed that time is relative to our frame of reference. Boltzmann and Gibbs suggested that the direction of time might well be derived from the behavior of aggregates of particles following laws of chance, rather than from behavior dependent on a prior assignment of the direction of time. Schrödinger drew the conclusion that perhaps the absolute is mind, not time: "...physical theory in its present stage strongly suggests the indestructibility of Mind by Time."[94] The ultimate One, Self and World, must by its nature be immortal, and by this argument Schrödinger hoped to strengthen our sense that it is also timeless.

8. CRITIQUE

Schrödinger's view of comprehensibility is by and large convincing, but his efforts to resolve the difficulties attendant on objectivation are not. In particular, his acceptance of the doctrine of identity is difficult to reconcile with his evident caring for his fellow human beings who can be missed,[95] and with his insistence that science is based on a belief in the existence of individual, responsible persons. There seem to be serious flaws in his

[91] *MVW*, p. 95.
[92] *MM*, p. 82.
[93] *Ibid.*, Ch. V.
[94] *Ibid.*, p. 87; see also my discussion on pp. 29–30 of Ch. II above.
[95] Consider, for instance, his complaint about modern technology, to the effect that the availability of transportation makes the resettling of families easier, but the high cost of travel keeps both old friends and relatives from seeing each other except at long intervals (*SH*, p. 3).

arguments, along with much insight to be treasured. Let us turn first to the grounds for disagreement with Schrödinger and then to his real contributions to our understanding of nature and the self.

To begin with, objectivation as Schrödinger described it—merely considering the world out there as an object of study—does not necessarily entail the absence of mind or selves from the external world. Schrödinger, perhaps without realizing it, has carried the principle of objectivation several steps further into what Michael Polanyi calls "objectivism." In objectivism a view of the world as out there is combined with (a) the assumption that all knowledge of it is to be found by precisely specifiable procedures of observation, measurement, and verification[96] and (b) the hypothesis that reality consists of nothing but a set of particles and forces, or some equivalent completely impersonal substrate.[97] Acceptance of these two further assertions would indeed eliminate mind or personality from the world view, and insofar as objectivation is taken to include these principles, Schrödinger is correct in claiming such elimination.

Schrödinger seems to have accepted uncritically this strict objectivist view of science, perhaps because he found it convenient to talk about its difficulties as a way of arguing for the doctrine of identity. If he had attempted a systematic presentation of his philosophy, he might have seen that such a narrow understanding of science is inconsistent with his view that science uses and must use "metaphysical" elements that go beyond the limits of strict logic. However, Schrödinger never attempted such a major synthesis, and this inconsistency, running through most of his nontechnical writings, remains a confusing element in his interpretation of the scientific world view.

A more consistent interpretation of science is possible. Here the analysis of Michael Polanyi is especially helpful. His argument is not so much a proposal for how science *should* function as it is a description of the *actual* state of our knowledge of living systems and of persons. Polanyi considers, for example, how biology operates in describing patterns of behavior in living things. He suggests that in our observation of biological organisms, even of such simple ones as amoebae, we recognize patterns of behavior to which we can also ascribe rules of rightness, and hence success or failure

[96] Polanyi describes the objectivist's observer as a "specifically functioning mindless knower," *Personal Knowledge*, p. 264.

[97] Another provocative description of the objectivist view, together with its origin in the history of consciousness, is that given by Owen Barfield in *Saving the Appearances*, cited above.

in living up to these rules. An amoeba normally flows around a food particle and successfully ingests it, but occasionally it is not able to do so. Hence the terms "success" and "failure" have a clear meaning. The important point is that we make judgments about the rules of rightness and the failure or success of biological achievements, which judgments are partly based on specifiable features of our observation and partly on unspecifiable tacit components of knowledge.[98]

Tacit components of knowledge are things we know but cannot describe. Their existence and functioning are central to Polanyi's thought. They include in the first place the perception of forms or *Gestalten*, whether sensed subconsciously or with considerable conscious effort at discernment. They also include the kind of knowledge we obtain from tools and instruments when they function for us as extensions of our bodies, furnishing clues from which we attend focally to an object of interest. It is by a combination of such types of tacit knowledge with articulate reasoning that complex judgments can be made in recognizing organic patterns of structure and achievement, or, in fact, in perceiving any sort of organizing principle.

As we go up the family tree of living things, we find more and more complex adaptive behavior. When we perceive patterns of behavior which we call purposive, we find ourselves able to ascribe consciousness to an organism.[99] At this point, the tacit component of perception becomes quite large. We "read" the existence of the mind of a dog or a cat, as we "read" meaning into a group of words or sentences. Our knowledge at this level is personal both because we exercise an unspecifiable art of judgment and because we relate personally to the animal.

In fact, as we come to deal with animals to whom we can relate in a personal way, we meet them more as I and Thou than as I and It, to use Martin Buber's terminology. As for human beings, it is in the I-Thou relationship that we come to know a person, to experience the cognizing and willing self of the other. The objectified world which contains no selves is a world met as It and not as Thou.

By giving up the idea that only specifiable and formally reproducible knowledge is allowable, by accepting forms, patterns, organisms, minds, persons, all as basic categories of reality, and by including the relation

[98] M. Polanyi, *The Study of Man* (Chicago: University of Chicago Press, 1959), pp. 11–39; "Tacit Knowing," ref. 26 above; and *The Tacit Dimension* (Garden City, N.Y.: Doubleday, 1966).

[99] M. Polanyi, *Personal Knowledge*, pp. 361–364.

of meeting between I and Thou along with the relation of observing between I and It, we restore personality to the objective world. It is an outlook of this sort which may overcome the depersonalization and loss of values of our modern culture.

Schrödinger very much wanted a world picture full of sensation, meaning, and personality, as well as of scientifically describable events in time and space. However, his attachment to objectivism led him to overemphasize what he called the scientific world view, a view which cannot have personality in it. Thus he made the problem of finding a satisfactory world view a good deal more complicated than is necessary.

In Schrödinger's own effort to restore the self to the world picture, he jumped all the way from objectivism to the doctrine of identity, from a world without persons or personality to a world in which persons are all submerged in a single Self. Since he did on occasion stress the centrality of form as opposed to substance, and referred to *Gestalt* as a primary category of explanation,[100] it is a pity that he did not himself pursue the *Gestalt* view to a point where he might find a place for persons in the comprehensible, objectified world.

Schrödinger's doctrine of identity is contradicted by his convincing association of consciousness with novelty, which leads to a strong sense of the newness and individuality of each person, to a multiplication of perceptions of the world, and to difficulties with the ideas of the timeless Self. This Self which Schrödinger says is identical with each of us is unchanging and eternal, the completely *habitual*, which by his description should therefore be completely *unconscious*. Nevertheless it is the conscious, willing "I" about whom he asserts the doctrine of identity with the Self as an answer to the question of Plotinus. There is a confusion of objects here. Such a Universal unconscious Self and the individual consciousness appreciating the novelty of life can not be the same entities. Schrödinger the Vedanta philosopher and Schrödinger the rational, scientific thinker have different objects in mind when they discourse on persons and selves.

The relation of consciousness and novelty has awkward consequences for determinism and timelessness, as Schrödinger has used these concepts. All our gaining of knowledge involves newness and is therefore creative. The solving of problems involves creative leaps of thought. A problem that can be solved by purely deductive logic becomes a mere formality, akin to substituting numbers in a formula. We jump a "logical gap" when

---

[100] *SH*, pp. 18–21; see also p. 76 of Ch. IV above.

a genuine problem is solved, and only in retrospect can we use deduction to verify that we are correct. Even constructing a proof involves a sense of newness. As George Polya noted, "When you have satisfied yourself that the theorem is true, you start proving it."[101] The original hunch that the theorem is true is a new insight; the proof is a verification, and even that has a quality of newness.

Creativity appears not only in problem solving but in every act of perception. Perception involves an effort to see something that was hitherto unknown. Every assertion of importance involves statements that have never been made before (when one considers their meaning and context and who it is who utters them). Language must have a wide range of indefiniteness in the meaning of its words and grammar, for otherwise nothing worth saying—nothing that can be recognized as having a specific meaning in a specific and therefore in some sense unique circumstance—could be said.[102] All of our basic experience is therefore creative and unpredictable. This is why any view of man as a causally determined being is scientifically unjustified—it contradicts all conscious experience, which is more evidence than is available for any other proposition.

The understanding of experience as creative leaves a clear place for Schrödinger's combination of causality and chance as elements of a *comprehensible* theory of the world. However, to the earlier comments on comprehensibility should be added the observation that creative adaptation to determined and accidental occurrences does not seem to be explainable solely in terms of causality and chance. Some additional category, such as that of action by comprehensive entities in the form of personal centers of knowing and doing, is needed to complete our scheme of explanation.[103]

Considerations of novelty and creativity do not remove timelessness from the world of experience. Many discoveries we make are of principles which possess no character of ever having come into being or ever being likely to disappear, even though our views about them may change. The law of conservation of energy, to whatever extent it *is* true, has always *been* true and always *will be*. In spite of the newness of daily experience,

---

[101] G. Polya, *Mathematics and Plausible Reasoning* (Princeton: Princeton University Press, 1954), II, 76.

[102] M. Polanyi, *Personal Knowledge*, p. 110.

[103] See the discussion on pp. 142–144 above, and M. Polanyi, *Personal Knowledge*, Ch. 12.

we still identify ourselves with the persons we have been since birth, and we still participate in timeless elements of our heritage and of the world in which we dwell.

Another problem with the doctrine of identity is that if each of us is a new and different aspect of the world, our several perceptions of an aspect of the world can no longer be considered to be one single occurrence. Rather, we can borrow Schrödinger's phrase and say that the world lights up to itself anew in each conscious creature. But would the existence of innumerable different perceptions of the world not bring us back to a belief in a plurality of worlds or in a nonobservable *Ding an sich* behind each of the perceptions?

I do not think so. The difficulty is not so serious as Schrödinger would have us believe. What misled him was that in his discussion of the problems of perception he used spatial categories in relating mind and world. He spoke of locating the world *in* the mind, of the mind as the stage on which the action of the world is carried out.[104] The world is *held in common*, is a *common constituent of perception*, not a common *object* of perception.[105] Schrödinger gave perception a kind of objective structure with a location. Precisely because the one world (existing and perceived) seems to have a location in the mind he thought there was a need for a doctrine of identity. In spite of Schrödinger's announced claim of getting away from Berkeleian idealism,[106] he fell into difficulties like those which have plagued the idealists. Had Schrödinger eschewed the spatial categories and described perception as an act, not as a thing with a location, he would have avoided idealism. If we forego any such spatial description, can we not say without contradiction that many minds can perceive the same world? Most of us are convinced that we perceive a world with the character of not only being "out there" but also of being common to all of us. Furthermore, we are aware of the incompleteness and possible errors of our separate acts of perception, so that the perceived world need not be perceived the same way by everyone. In this view, there still is only *the* world. The world that each of us perceives imperfectly and partially is the real one.

In spite of the limitations of his arguments, Schrödinger has provided us with insights of permanent value on the relation of each self to the nature of which we are intimate parts and which has brought us into

---

[104] "On the Peculiarity of the Scientific World View," *WIL*, p. 226; *WN*, p. 83.
[105] E. Schrödinger, "Seek for the Road," *MVW*, p. 16.
[106] *Ibid.*, p. 31.

being. He has demonstrated our deep unity with the world and the necessity of accepting our personal relation to it as part of its very nature and our own. He has opened up the mystery of the individual self and the reality to which we are all related, a mystery which points beyond all philosophical argument.

If it is felt that any such alleged relation of world and self should be rejected as beyond demonstration, we should consider with Schrödinger whether the alternative "scientific" view of a real world of unobservable ultimate particles that interact with our sense organs to produce the phenomena of experience is not equally beyond proof. Schrödinger argued that *each* type of view is both metaphysical (because there is no way to verify the claim) and mystical (because it refers to alleged relations between different categories of being, mind, and world).

Schrödinger believed that only by putting the self back into the world could we restore values to their proper place, for values are held by persons.[107] In returning the self to the world we also restore the possibility of finding God: "A personal God cannot have a place in a world-picture that only became accessible at the price of removing from it everything personal. We know that whenever God is experienced, He is an experience as real as an immediate sense perception, as real as one's own personality. Just like the latter He must be absent from the spatial-temporal picture. 'I do not encounter God in space and time,' so speaks the honest scientific thinker and is taken to task for it by those in whose catechism it says: 'God is spirit.'"[108]

Schrödinger was deeply concerned with the unification of thought and knowledge in general, quite beyond the particular questions of self and world (see Ch. I). He spoke of the wall now dividing the "Two Cultures" (to use C. P. Snow's term), a wall which separates "the 'two paths', that of the heart and that of pure reason. We look back along the wall: could we not pull it down, has it always been there? As we scan its windings over hills and vales back in history we behold a land far, far, away at a space of over two thousand years back, where the wall flattens and disappears and the path was not yet split, but was only *one*."[109]

Science and religion have been traditionally on opposite sides of the wall. Today there appears to be a truce, but the truce

---

[107] *NG*, pp. 94–95 and *WIL*, p. 108; "On the Peculiarity of the Scientific World View," *WIL*, p. 227; *WN*, p. 84.

[108] "On the Peculiarity of the Scientific World View," *WIL*, p. 228; *WN*, p. 85.

[109] *NG*, p. 11.

was not reached by setting in harmony with one another the two kinds of outlook, the strictly scientific and the metaphysical, but rather by a resolve to ignore each other, little short of contempt.... It is pathetically amusing to observe how on the one side only scientific information is taken seriously, while the other side ranges science among men's worldly activities, whose findings are less momentous and have, as a matter of course, to give way when at variance with the superior insight gained in a different fashion, by pure thought or revelation. One regrets to see mankind strive towards the same goal along two different and difficult winding paths, with blinkers and separating walls, and with little attempt to join all forces and to achieve, if not a full understanding of nature and the human situation, at least the soothing recognition of the intrinsic unity of our search.[110]

Schrödinger commented on the tragedy of the separation and the obvious consequence of the reduction of "the range of what could be attained if all the thinking power at our disposal"[111] could be pooled without bias. Even more disturbing, however, is the dual situation of the individual man. Humanity is not really divided into two different crowds who follow different paths, but into groups of individuals with concerns that bridge the separation:

> Many of us are not decided which path to follow. With regret, nay with despair, many find that they have to shut themselves off alternately from the one and from the other kind of outlook. It is certainly not in general the case that by acquiring a good all-round scientific education you so completely satisfy the innate longing for a religious or philosophical stabilization, in face of the vicissitudes of everyday life, as to feel quite happy without anything more. What does happen often is that science suffices to jeopardize popular religious convictions, but not to replace them by anything else. This produces the grotesque phenomenon of scientifically trained, highly competent minds with an unbelievably childlike—undeveloped or atrophied—philosophical outlook.[112]

Schrödinger's own attempts to bridge the wall, or better to tear it down, constitute a modest but stimulating addition to the many contemporary efforts in this direction. He failed in finding adequate answers to his own questions but failed in the way of dreaming a great dream. He was a true scientist in always keeping open to new insights, describing, in fact, this aspect of the scientific attitude as being in contrast to the efforts of the religiously inclined who seek a closed view of the world that would

[110] *Ibid.*, pp. 9–10.
[111] *Ibid.*, p. 10.
[112] *Ibid.*

protect their views and institutions. Such people are tempted to prematurely fill gaps in scientific knowledge by special hypotheses which contradict scientific method in not taking into account the widest and best accepted generalizations that have already been attained.[113]

On the other hand, the integrity of science involves leaving many phenomena unexplained until the progress of science can adequately take care of them. "The steadfastness in standing up to a *non liquet*, nay in appreciating it as a stimulus and a signpost to further quest, is a natural and indispensable disposition in the mind of a scientist."[114]

Erwin Schrödinger continued throughout his life to appreciate the mystery and paradox at the depths of life. No matter how absorbed he became in his search for truth, for answers to the questions of nature and the self, he refused to fill the open gaps with spurious or shoddy arguments.

> The world is big and great and beautiful. My scientific knowledge of the events in it comprises hundreds of millions of years. Yet in another way it is ostensibly contained in a poor seventy or eighty or ninety years granted to me—a tiny spot in immeasurable time, nay even in the finite millions and and milliards of years that I have learnt to measure and to assess. Whence come I and whither go I? That is the great unfathomable question, the same for every one of us. Science has no answer to it. Yet science represents the level best we have been able to ascertain in the way of safe and incontrovertible knowledge.
>
> However, our life as something like human beings has lasted, at the most, only about half a million years. From all that we know, we may anticipate, even on this particular globe, quite a few million years to come. And from all this we feel that any thought we attain to during this time will not have been thought in vain.[115]

[113] *Ibid.*, pp. 6–8; see also pp. 123–124 above.
[114] *Ibid.*, p. 6.
[115] *Ibid.*, pp. 95–96.

Bibliography

1. BOOKS BY ERWIN SCHRÖDINGER

1927   *Abhandlungen zur Wellenmechanik.* Leipzig: J. A. Barth. 2nd edition with additional papers, Leipzig: J. A. Barth, 1928.

       Collected Papers on Wave Mechanics. Translated into English from the 2nd edition by J. F. Shearer and W. M. Deans. London: Blackie and Son, Ltd., 1928.

       Mémoires sur la Mécanique ondulatoire. Translated into French by A. Proca with an introduction by the author and notes specially written for this translation. Paris: F. Alcan, 1933.

1928   *Four Lectures on Wave Mechanics, delivered at the Royal Institution, London, on 5th, 7th, 12th, and 14th March, 1928, by Dr. Erwin Schrödinger.* London: Blackie and Son, Ltd.

       Vier Vorlesungen über Wellenmechanik. Translated into German by Hans Klopfermann. Berlin: J. Springer, 1928.

1932   *Über Indeterminismus in der Physik; Ist die Naturwissenschaft milieubedingt? Zwei Vorträge zur Kritik der naturwissenschaftlichen Erkenntnis.* Leipzig: J. A. Barth.

1935   *Science and the Human Temperament.* A collection of papers translated into English by James Murphy and W. H. Johnston with a biographical introduction by James Murphy and a foreword by Lord Rutherford of Nelson. New York: W. W. Norton and Co., Inc. and London: Allen and Unwin, Ltd.

1944   *What Is Life? The Physical Aspect of the Living Cell.* Cambridge: Cambridge University Press. 2nd edition, 1952. Translated into German by Ludwig Mazurcak and Ernest Schneider. Bern: A. Francke A. G., and Munich: Lehnen, 1946. 2nd edition, 1951.

       Translated into Spanish by Greta Mayena. Buenos Aires: Espasa-Calpe, 1948.

       Translated into French by Leon Keffler. Paris: Le Club français du livre, 1949. Brussels: Éditions de la Paix: 1950.

       Translated into Japanese by Yasuo Shizume. Tokyo: Iwanami shoten, 1951.

1946 *Statistical Thermodynamics: A Course of Seminar Lectures delivered in January–March 1944 at the School of Theoretical Physics, Dublin Institute for Advanced Studies by Erwin Schrödinger.* Cambridge: Cambridge University Press, 1946. 2nd edition, 1952.

Translated into German by W. Bloch. Leipzig: J. Barth, 1952.

1949 *Gedichte.* Godesberg [now Düsseldorf]: Kupper.

1950 *Space-Time Structure.* Cambridge: Cambridge University Press.

1951 *Science and Humanism: Physics in Our Time.* Cambridge: Cambridge University Press, 1951.

Translated into German. [No translator listed.] Wien: Deuticke, 1951.

Translated into Italian by Piero Lantermo. Florence: Sansoni, 1953.

Translated into Spanish by Ignacio Bolívar. Madrid: Alhambra, 1954.

Translated into French by J. Ladrière. Bruges and Paris: Desclée de Brouwer, 1954.

Translated into Japanese by Kôji Fushimi *et al.* Tokyo: Misuzu shobô, 1956.

1954. *Nature and the Greeks.* Cambridge: Cambridge University Press.

Translated into German by Mira Koffka. Wien: Zsolnay, 1955. Hamburg: Rowohlt, 1956. Hamburg and Wien: Zsolnay (Jubiläumsausg), 1959.

1956 *Expanding Universes.* Cambridge: Cambridge University Press.

What Is Life? and Other Scientific Essays. Garden City, New York: Doubleday Anchor Books.

1957 *Science Theory and Man*—Reprint of *Science and the Human Temperament* with the addition of "What is an Elementary Particle?" New York: Dover Publications, Inc., 1957, and London: Allen and Unwin, 1958.

1958 *Mind and Matter.* Cambridge: Cambridge University Press. Translated into German by W. Westphal. Braunschweig: Vieweg, 1959.

1961 *Meine Weltansicht.* Hamburg: P. Zsolnay. Translated into English by Cecily Hastings as *My View of the World.* Cambridge: Cambridge University Press, 1964.

1962 *Was ist ein Naturgesetz? Beiträge zum naturwissenschaftlichen Weltbild.* München/Wien: R. Oldenbourg.

1963 *Briefe zur Wellenmechanik.* Correspondence with Planck, Einstein, and Lorentz. Vienna: Springer, 1963.

2. ARTICLES BY ERWIN SCHRÖDINGER

1910 "Über die Leitung der Elektrizität auf der Oberfläche von Isolatoren zu feuchter Luft," *S. B. Akad. Wiss. Wien,* Abt. 2a, **119**, 1215–1222.

Bibliography

1912 "Zur kinetischen Theorie des Magnetismus," *S. B. Akad. Wiss. Wien,* Abt. 2a, **121**, 1305–1328.

"Studien über Kinetik der Dielektrika, den Schmelzpunkt, Pyro- und Piezoelektrizität," *S. B. Akad Wiss. Wien,* Abt. 2a, **121**, 1937– 1972.

"Über die Höhenverteilung der durchdringenden atmosphärischen Strahlung. (Theorie.) Beiträge zur Kenntnis der atmosphärischen Elektrizität XLVIII," *S. B. Akad. Wiss. Wien,* Abt. 2a, **121**, 2391–2406.

1913 "Notiz über die Theorie der anomalen elektrischen Dispersion," *Verhandl. deut. physik. Ges.,* **15**, 1167–1172. (Same as Vol. 11 of *Berichte deut. physik. Ges.*)

"Radium-A Gehalt der Atmosphäre in Seeham 1913," *S. B. Akad. Wiss. Wien,* Abt. 2a, **122**, 2023–2067.

1914 (With K. W. F. Kohlrausch.) "Über die weiche (β) Sekundärstrahlung von γ-Strahlen," *S. B. Akad. Wiss. Wien.,* Abt. 2a, **123**, 1319–1367.

"Zur Dynamik der elastischen Punktreihe," *S. B. Akad. Wiss. Wien.,* Abt. 2a, **123**, 1679–1696.

"Über die Schärfe der mit Röntgenstrahlen erzeugten Interferenz- bilder," *Physik. Z.,* **15**, 79–86.

"Zur Theorie des Debyeeffekts," *Physik. Z.,* **15**, 497–503.

"Zur Dynamik elastisch gekoppelter Punktsysteme," *Ann. Physik,* **44**, 916–934.

1915 "Notiz über den Kapillardruck in Gasblasen," *Ann. Physik,* **46**, 413–418.

"Zur Theorie der Fall- und Steigversuche an Teilchen mit Brown'scher Bewegung," *Physik. Z.,* **16**, 289–295.

1917 "Die Ergebnisse der neueren Forschung über Atom- und Molekular- wärmen," *Naturwissenschaften,* **5**, 537–543 and 561–567.

"Zur Akustik der Atmosphäre," *Physik. Z.,* **18**, 445–453.

1918 "Die Energiekomponenten des Gravitationsfeldes," *Physik. Z.,* **19**, 4–7.

"Über ein Lösungssystem der allgemeinen kovarianten Gravitations- gleichungen," *Physik. Z.,* **19**, 20–22.

"Über ein in der experimentellen Radiumforschung auftretendes Problem der statistischen Dynamik," *S. B. Akad. Wiss. Wien.,* Abt. 2a, **127**, 237–262.

"Notiz über die Ordnung in Zufallsreihen," *Physik. Z.,* **19**, 218–220.

"Dielektrizität," in *Handbuch der Elektrizität und des Magnetismus,* ed. Leo Graetz (Leipzig: J. A. Barth), I, 157–231.

1919 "Der Energieinhalt der Festkörper im Lichte der neueren Forschung," *Physik. Z.*, **20**, 420–428, 450–455, 474–480, 497–503, and 523–526.

"Über die Kohärenz in weitgeöffneten Bündeln," *Ann. Physik*, **61**, 69–86.

"Wahrscheinlichkeitstheoretische Studien, betreffend Schweidler'sche Schwankungen, besonders die Theorie der Messanordung," *S. B. Akad. Wiss. Wien.*, Abt., 2a, **128**, 177–237.

1920 "Theorie der Pigmente von grösster Leuchtkraft," *Ann. Physik*, **62**, 603–622.

"Farbenmetrik," *Z. Physik*, **1**, 459–466.

"Grundlinien einer Theorie der Farbenmetrik im Tagessehen," *Ann. Physik*, **63**, 397–426, 427–456, and 481–520.

1921 "Versuch zur modelmässigen Deutung des Terms der scharfen Nebenserien," *Z. Physik*, **4**, 347–354.

"Isotopie und Gibbssches Paradoxon," *Z. Physik*, **5**, 163–166.

1922 "Dopplerprinzip und Bohrsche Frequenzbedingung," *Physik. Z.*, **23**, 301–303.

"Über die spezifische Wärme fester Körper bei höher Temperatur und über die Quantelung von Schwingungen endlicher Amplitude," *Z. Physik*, **11**, 170–176.

"Über eine bemerkenswerte Eigenschaft der Quantenbahnen eines einzelnen Elektrons," *Z. Physik*, **12**, 13–23.

1924 "Gasentartung und mittlere Weglänger," *Physik. Z.*, **25**, 41–45.

"Über das thermische Gleichgewicht zwischen Licht- und Schallstrahlen," *Physik. Z.*, **25**, 89–94.

"Bohrs neue Strahlungshypothese und der Energiesatz," *Naturwissenschaften*, **12**, 720–724.

"Über den Ursprung der Empfindlichkeitskurven des Auges," *Naturwissenschaften*, **12**, 925–929.

"Bemerkung zu zwei Arbeiten des Herrn Elemér Császár über Strahlungstheorie und spezifische Wärmen," *Z. Physik*, **25**, 173–174.

"Über die Rotationswärme des Wasserstoffs," *Z. Physik.*, **30**, 341–349.

1925 "Die Wasserstoffähnlichen Spektren vom Standpunkt der Polarisierbarkeit des Atomrumpfes," *Ann. Physik.*, **77**, 43–70.

"Die Erfüllbarkeit der Relativitätsforderung in der klassischen Mechanik," *Ann. Physik.*, **77**, 325–336.

"Bemerkungen über die statistische Entropiedefinition beim idealen Gas," *S. B. Preuss. Akad. Wiss.*, pp. 434–441. Additional printing commissioned by the Akademie d. Wissenschaften, Berlin: W. de Gruyter & Co., 1925.

Bibliography

"Über die subjektiven Sternfarben und die Qualität der Dämmerungs-
empfindungen," *Naturwissenschaften*, **13**, 373–376.

"Über Farbenmessung," *Physik. Z.*, **26**, 349–352.

"Über das Verhältnis der Vierfarben- zur Dreifarbentheorie," *S. B.
Akad. Wiss. Wien.*, Abt. 2a, **134**, 471–490. Additional printing commis-
sioned by the Akademie d. Wissenschaft in Wien: Hölder-Pichler-
Tempsky, 1925.

1926   "Die Gesichtsempfindungen," in *Müller-Pouillets Lehrbüch der Physik*
(11th ed.; Braunschweig: Vieweg), II, Part 1, 456–460.

"Die Energiestufen des idealen einatomigen Gasmodells," *S. B. Preuss.
Akad. Wiss.*, 23–26. Additional printing commissioned by the Akademie
d. Wissenschaften, Berlin: W. de Gruyter & Co., 1926.

"Zur Einsteinschen Gastheorie," *Physik. Z.*, **27**, 95–101.

(With K. W. F. Kohlrausch.) "Die Ehrenfestche Modell der H-Kurve,"
Physik. Z., **27**, 306–313.

"Spezifische Wärme (theoretischer Teil)," in *Handbuch der Physik*, ed.
H. Geiger and K. Scheel (Berlin: Julius Springer, 1926), **10**, 275–320.

"Quantisierung als Eigenwertproblem, I," *Ann. Physik.*, **79**, 361–376.
Reprinted in *WM*, pp. 1–12, and *AW*, pp. 1–16.

"Quantisierung als Eigenwertproblem, II," *Ann. Physik*, **79**, 489–527.
Reprinted in *WM*, pp. 13–40, and *AW*, pp. 16–55.

"Der stetige Übergang von der Mikro- zur Makromechanik,"
Naturwissenschaften, **14**, 664–666. Reprinted in *WM*, pp. 41–44, and *AW*,
pp. 56–61.

"Über das Verhältnis der Heisenberg-Born-Jordanschen Quantenmechanik zu der meinen," *Ann. Physik.*, **79**, 734–756. Reprinted in *WM*,
pp. 45–61, and *AW*, pp. 62–84.

"Quantisierung als Eigenwertproblem, III," *Ann. Physik.*, **80**, 437–490.
Reprinted in *WM*, pp. 62–101, and *AW*, pp. 85–138.

"Quantisierung als Eigenwertproblem, IV," *Ann. Physik.*, **81**, 109–139.
Reprinted in *WM*, pp. 102–123, and *AW*, pp. 139–169.

"An Undulatory Theory of the Mechanics of Atoms and Molecules,"
Phys. Rev., **28**, 1049–1070.

1927   "Über den Comptoneffekt," *Ann. Physik*, **82**, 257–264. Reprinted in
WM, pp. 124–129, and *AW*, pp. 170–177.

"Der Energieimpulssatz der Materiewellen," *Ann. Physik.*, **82**, 265–272.
Reprinted in *WM*, pp. 130–136, and *AW*, pp. 178–185.

"Energieaustausch nach der Wellenmechanik," *Ann. Physik.*, **83**, 956–
968. Reprinted in *WM*, pp. 137–146, and *AW*, pp. 186–198.

1928 "Neue Wege in der Physik," *Elektrische Nachrichten-Technik*, **5**, 485–488. Also in *Elektrotechnische Zeitschrift*, **50**, 15–16, (1929).

"Der Erkenntnistheoretische Wert physikalisches Modellvorstellungen," *Jahresbericht des physikalischen Vereins Frankfurt am Main*, 1928/9, 44–51.

Trans. W. H. Johnston as "Conceptual Models in Physics and Their Philosophical Value," in *SHT*, pp. 148–165. Also in STM, same pp.

1929 "Was ist ein Naturgesetz?" *Naturwissenschaften*, **17**, 9–11; *WN*, pp. 9–17. Trans. J. Murphy as "What Is a Law of Nature?" *SHT* and *STM*, pp. 133–147.

"Die Erfassung der Quantengesetze durch kontinuierliche Funktionen," *Naturwissenschaften*, **17**, 486–489.

"Antrittsrede," *S. B. Preuss. Akad. Wiss.*, pp. C–CII. Trans. J. Murphy in biographical introduction to *SHT*, pp. xiii–xviii; *STM*, same pp.

"Verwaschene Eigenwertspektra," *S. B. Preuss. Akad. Wiss.*, pp. 668–682. Additional printing commissioned by the Akademie d. Wissenschaften: Berlin: W. de Gruyter & Co., 1929.

[Unsigned.] "Addresse an Herrn Max Planck zum 50. Doktorjubiläum am 28. Juni 1929," *S. B. Preuss. Akad. Wiss.*, Philos.-Hist. Klasse, pp. 431–432.

"Die Wandlung des physikalischen Weltbegriffs," lecture at the Deutschen Museum, München, May 6; in *WN*, pp. 18–26.

1930 "Zum Heisenbergschen Unschärfeprinzip," *S. B. Preuss. Akad. Wiss.*, pp. 296–303. Additional printing commissioned by the Akademie d. Wissenschaften: Berlin: W. de Gruyter & Co., 1930.

"Über die kraftefreie Bewegung in der relativistischen Quantenmechanik," *S. B. Preuss. Akad. Wiss.*, pp. 418–428. Additional printing commissioned by the Akademie d. Wissenschaften: Berlin: W. de Gruyter & Co., 1930.

1931 "Zur Quantendynamik des Elektrons," *S. B. Preuss. Akad. Wiss.*, pp. 63–72.

"Über die Umkehrung der Naturgesetze," *S. B. Preuss. Akad. Wiss.*, pp. 144–153.

"Spezielle Relativitätstheorie und Quantenmechanik," *S. B. Preuss. Akad. Wiss.*, pp. 238–247. Reprinted by Commission of the Akademie der Wissenschaften, Berlin: W. de Gruyter & Co., 1931.

"Bemerkungen zu der Arbeit von V. Fock 'Die inneren Freiheitsgrade des Elektrons,'" *Z. Physik*, **70**, 808–811.

1932 "Diracsches Elektron im Schwerefeld," *S. B. Preuss. Akad. Wiss.*, 105–128. Additional printing commissioned by the Akademie der Wissenschaften, Berlin: W. de Gruyter and Co., 1932.

Bibliography

"Sur la théorie relativiste de l'électron et l'interprétation de la mécanique quantique," *Ann. Inst. Henri Poincaré*, **2**, 269–310.

(With H. R. von Traubenberg and R. Gebauer.) "Über das Verhalten des Starkeffektes bei plötzlichen Feldänderungen," *Z. Physik.*, **78**, 309–317.

"Anmerkungen zum Kausalproblem," *Erkennthis*, **3**, 65–70.

1933   "Warum sind die Atome so klein?," *Forsch. u. Fortschr.*, **9**, 125–126.

"Über den zweiten Hauptsatz der Thermodynamik," *S. B. Preuss. Akad. Wiss.*, p. 165. (Abstract only.)

1934   "Die Grundgedanken der Wellenmechanik," in *Die Moderne Atomtheorie; die bei der Entgegennahme des Nobelpreises 1933 in Stockholm gehaltenen Vorträge.* With W. Heisenberg and P. A. M. Dirac. (Leipzig: S. Hirzel), pp. 19–36. Also printed in *Les Prix Nobel en 1933*, M. C. G. Santesson, ed. (Stockholm: Imprimerie Royale, P. A. Norstedt-söner, 1935), "Les Conférences Nobel," pp. 1–13 and *WN*, pp. 86–101, Trans. J. Murphy as "The Fundamental Idea of Wave Mechanics," and reprinted in *SHT* and *STM*, pp. 166–192.

"Über die Unanwendbarkeit der Geometrie im Kleinen," *Naturwissenschaften*, **22**, 518–520.

1935   "Erwin Schrödinger," autobiographical sketch in *Les Prix Nobel en 1933*, M. C. G. Santesson, ed. (Stockholm: Imprimerie Royale, P. A. Norstedt-söner), pp. 86–88.

(With Max Born.) "The Absolute Field Constant in the New Field Theory," *Nature*, **135**, 342.

"Die gegenwärtige Situation in der Quantenmechanik," *Naturwissenschaften*, **23**, 807–812, 823–828, and 844–849.

"Discussion of Probability Relations Between Separated Systems," *Proc. Cambridge Phil. Soc.*, **31**, 555–563.

"La Nueva Mecanica Ondulatoria," *Cursos de la Universidad internacional de Verano en Santander* (Madrid), 29–36.

"Quelques remarques au sujet des bases de la connaissance scientifique," *Scientia* (Bologna), **57**, 181–191.

"Physical Science and the Temper of the Age." First published in *SHT*, pp. 106–132; also *STM*, same pp.

"Science, Art, and Play," *The Philosopher* (London), **13**, 11–18. Reprinted in *SHT* and *STM*, pp. 27–38.

"Contribution to Born's New Theory of the Electromagnetic Field," *Proc. Roy. Soc. A*, **150**, 465–477.

"The Law of Chance: The Problem of Causation in Modern Science." First published in *SHT*, pp. 39–51; *STM*, same pp.

1936 "Probability Relations Between Separated Systems," *Proc. Cambridge Phil. Soc.*, **32**, 446–452.

"Phenomenological Theory of Supra-Conductivity," *Nature*, **137**, 824.

"Indeterminism and Free Will," *Nature*, **138**, 13–14.

1937 "Eigenschwingungen des Sphärischen Raums," *Acta Pontif. Acad. Sci.*, **2**, No. 9, 321–364.

1938 "Die Mehrdeutigkeit der Wellenfunktion," *Ann. Physik.*, **32**, 49–55.

"Sur la théorie du monde d'Eddington," *Nuovo Cimento*, **15**, 246–254.

"Mean Free Path of Protons in the Universe," *Nature*, **141**, 410.

1939 "The Proper Vibrations of the Expanding Universe," *Physica*, **6**, 899–912.

"Nature of the Nebular Red-shift," *Nature*, **144**, 593.

1940 "A Method of Determining Quantum-Mechanical Eigenvalues and Eigenfunctions," *Proc. R. Irish Acad.*, **46**A, 9–16.

"Maxwell's and Dirac's Equations in the Expanding Universe," *Proc. R. Irish Acad.*, **46**A, 25–44.

(With T. S. Broderick.) "Boolean Algebra and Probability Theory," *Proc. R. Irish Acad.*, **46**A, 103–112.

"The General Theory of Relativity and Wave Mechanics," *Wis-en-natuurkundig Tijdschrift*, **10**, 2–9. Also printed in *Scientific Papers Presented to Max Born* (New York: Hafner, 1953), and Edinburgh: Oliver and Boyd, 1953, pp. 65–74.

1941 "Obituary for Prof. Richard Bär," *Nature*, **147**, 536.

"Der Aufbau des Universums und der Aufbau der Materie," *Bull. Soc. Philomath. Paris*, **123**, 26–30.

"Further Studies on Solving Eigenvalue Problems by Factorization," *Proc. R. Irish. Acad.*, **46**A, 183–206.

"On the Solutions of Wave Equations for Non-vanishing Rest-mass Including a Source Function," *Proc. R. Irish. Acad.*, **47**A, 1–23.

(With J. Hamilton.) "Exchange and Spin," *Proc. R. Irish Acad.*, **47**A, 39–52.

"Factorization of the Hypergeometric Equation," *Proc. R. Irish Acad.*, **47**A, 53–54.

1942 "Non-linear Optics," *Proc. R. Irish Acad.*, **47**A, 77–117.

"Dynamics and Scattering Power of Born's Electron," *Proc. R. Irish Acad.*, **48**A, 91–122.

1943 "Pentads, Tetrads, and Triads of Meson-Matrices," *Proc. R. Irish Acad.*, **48**A, 135–146.

Bibliography

"Systematics of Meson-Matrices," *Proc. R. Irish Acad.*, **49**A, 29–42.

"The General Unitary Theory of the Physical Fields," *Proc. R. Irish Acad.*, **49**A, 43–58.

"A New Exact Solution in Non-linear Optics, (Two Wave System)," *Proc. R. Irish Acad.*, **49**A, 59–66.

"The Earth's and the Sun's Permanent Magnetic Fields in the Unitary Field Theory," *Proc. R. Irish Acad.*, **49**A, 135–148.

1944 "The Affine Connexion in Physical Field Theories," *Nature*, **153**, 572–575.

"Rate of *n*-fold Coincidences," *Nature*, **153**, 592–593.

"The Statistical Law in Nature," *Nature*, **153**, 704–705.

"The Point Charge in the Unitary Field Theory," *Proc. R. Irish Acad.*, **49**A, 225–235.

"Unitary Field Theory: Conservation Identities and Relation to Weyl and Eddington," *Proc. R. Irish Acad.*, **49**A, 237–244.

(With J. McConnell.) "The Shielding Effect of Planetary Magnetic Fields," *Proc. R. Irish Acad.*, **49**A, 259–273.

"The Union of the Three Fundamental Fields (Gravitation, Meson, Electromagnetism)," *Proc. R. Irish Acad.*, **49**A, 275–287.

1945 "On Distant Affine Connexion," *Proc. R. Irish Acad.*, **50**A, 143–154.

(With F. Mautner.) "Infinitesimal Affine Connexions with Twofold Einstein-Bargmann Symmetry," *Proc. R. Irish Acad.*, **50**A, 223–231.

"Probability Problems in Nuclear Chemistry," *Proc. R. Irish Acad.*, **51**A, 1–8.

1946 "Affine Feldtheorie und Meson," *Verhandlungen der Schweizerische Naturforschende Gesellschaft*, **126**, 53–61.

"The General Affine Field Laws," *Proc. R. Irish Acad.*, **51**A, 41–50.

"Der Geist der Naturwissenschaft," *Eranos Jahrbuch* (Zurich: Rhein, 1947), XIV (1946), 491–520. Published in English as "The Spirit of Science" in *Spirit and Nature, Papers from the Eranos Yearbooks* (Bollingen Series XXX. 1, New York: Pantheon Books, 1954), pp. 322–341. Reprinted in *WIL*, pp. 229–250.

1947 "Die Besonderheit des Weltbilds der Naturwissenschaft," *Acta Phys. Austriaca*, **1**, 201–245, and *WN*, pp. 27–85. Published in English as "On the Peculiarity of the Scientific World-View," *WIL*, pp. 178–228.

"The Foundation of the Theory of Probability, I," *Proc. R. Irish Acad.*, **51**A, 51–66.

"The Foundation of the Theory of Probability, II," *Proc. R. Irish Acad.*, **51**A, 141–150.

"The Relation Between Metric and Affinity," *Proc. R. Irish Acad.*, **51**A, 147–150.

"The Final Affine Field Laws, I," *Proc. R. Irish Acad.*, **51**A, 163–171.

1948 "2400 Jahre Quantentheorie," *Ann. Physik.*, (6) **3**, 43–48.

"The Final Affine Field Laws, II." *Proc. R. Irish Acad.*, **51**A, 205–216.

"The Final Affine Field Laws, III," *Proc. R. Irish Acad.*, **52**A, 1–9.

1950 "Irreversibility," *Proc. R. Irish Acad.*, **53**A, 189–195.

"The Future of Understanding," Three BBC talks on September 16, 23, 30, 1950. Published in *WIL*, pp. 118–131, also as Chapter II of *MM*.

"What is an Elementary Particle?" *Endeavour*, **9**, 109–116. Reprinted in *STM*, pp. 193–223, and in Smithsonian Institution's *Annual Report, 1950* (Washington, 1951), pp. 183–196. German translation as "Was ist ein Elementarteilchen?" in *WN*, pp. 121–143.

1951 (With A. Papapetrou.) "The Point-Charge in the Non-symmetric Field Theory," *Nature*, **168**, 40–41.

"On the Differential Identities of an Affinity," *Proc. R. Irish Acad.*, **54**A, 79–85.

"Studies in the Non-symmetric Generalization of the Theory of Gravitation, I," *Communications of the Dublin Institute for Advanced Studies*, Series A, 28 pp.

(With O. Hittmair), "Studies in the Generalized Theory of Gravitation, II: The Velocity of Light," *Communications of the Dublin Institute for Advanced Studies*, Series A, No. 8, 15 pp.

"A Combinatorial Problem in Counting Cosmic Rays," *Proc. Phys. Soc.*, A, **64**, 1040–1041.

1952 "Are There Quantum Jumps?" *Brit. J. Philos. Sci.*, **3**, 109–123 and 233–247. Reprinted in *WIL*, pp. 132–160.

"Unsere Vorstellung von der Materie" in *L'homme devant la Science* (Proceedings of the Rencontres Internationales de Genève, 1952, Neuchâtel: Éditions de Baconnière, 1952), pp. 37–54. Reprinted in *Naturw. Rund.*, **7** (1954), pp. 277–282, and *WN*, pp. 102–120. Trans. as "Our Conception of Matter," *WIL*, pp. 161–177. Another translation, "Our Image of Matter," is included with discussions of P. Auger, M. Born and W. Heisenberg in *On Modern Physics*, trans. M. Goodman and J. W. Binns (New York: Collier Books, 1952), pp. 45–66. A shortened version appeared in 1953 as "What is Matter?" *Scientific American*, **89**, 52–57.

"Dirac's New Electrodynamics," *Nature*, **169**, 538.

Bibliography

"Relativistic Fourier Reciprocity and the Elementary Masses," *Proc. R. Irish Acad.*, **55A**, 29–50.

1953 "La Signification de la Mécanique Ondulatoire" in *Louis de Broglie, Physicien et Penseur* (Paris: Albin Michel), pp. 16–32. "The Meaning of Wave Mechanics" (English translation) appears on facing pages.

1954 "Relativistic Quantum Theory," *Brit. J. Philos. Sci.*, **4**, 328–329. Extract from a private letter.

"Orientierung im Weltall," *Das Internationale Forum; Berichte und Stellungnahmen*, **3** (Zurich: Fontana, 1954), 7–31. Four speeches: "Orientierung im Weltall," "Erdalter und Weltalter," "Die Kohlenstoff-Uhr," und "Raum und Zeit."

"Measurement of Length and Angle in Quantum Mechanics," *Nature*, **173**, 442.

"Electric Charge and Current Engendered by Combined Maxwell–Einstein-Fields," *Proc. R. Irish Acad.*, **56A**, 13–21.

1955 "The Philosophy of Experiment," *Nuovo Cimento*, **1**, 5–15.

"A Thermodynamic Relation between Frequency Shift and Broadening," *Nuovo Cimento*, **1**, 63–69.

"Die Atomisten," *Merkur*, **9**, 815–824.

"The Wave Equation for Spin 1 in Hamiltonian Form, I," *Proc. Roy. Soc.*, A, **229**, 39–43.

(With L. Bass) "Must the Photon Mass be Zero?" *Proc. Roy. Soc.*, A, **232**, 1–6. Abstract is reprinted with discussion in *Nuovo Cimento Supplement*, (10) **4** (1956), 825–826.

"The Wave Equation for Spin 1 in Hamiltonian Form, II," *Proc. Roy. Soc.* A, **232**, 435–437.

1958 "Might Perhaps Energy be a Merely Statistical Concept?" *Nuovo Cimento*, **9**, 162–170.

Name Index

163

Name Index

Name Index

165

Subject Index